AIRBORNE EARLY WARNING

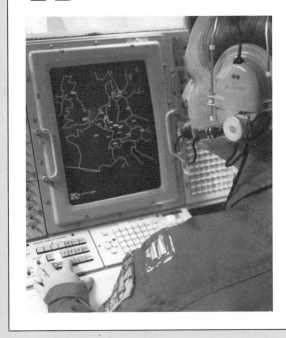

AIRBORNE EARLY WARNING

Design, development and operations

Mike Hirst

Published in 1983 by Osprey Publishing Limited
12–14 Long Acre, London WC2E 9LP
Member company of the George Philip Group

British Library Cataloguing in Publication Data

Hirst, Mike
    Airborne early warning.
    1. Airborne warning and control systems—History
    1. Title
    358.4′5   UG730

ISBN 0–85045–532–4

Editor Dennis Baldry
Designed by Roger Daniels
Filmset and printed in Great Britain
by BAS Printers Limited
Over Wallop, Hampshire

Contents

A Royal Flying Corps Bristol
Fighter patrols under a
leaden sky during the First
World War.

Chapter 1
Death of the Dawn Patrol

Aviation has lost a lot of its romanticism in recent years. Those who mourn the passing of its golden eras are often quick to put the blame on technology. But when we board an airliner to our package-holiday destination we expect all the benefits that technology can bring. We expect to travel in comfort, to arrive without mishap, and even if our sun-drenched paradise is temporarily shrouded in fog, we have become accustomed to landing on the correct runway.

Today, military aviation is just as sophisticated. In many cases even more so, as its requirements can establish technologies that airliners adopt in due course. Military leaders know that they must move with the times, or face the risk of imperilling their nation's defences.

Ever since military aircraft became a reality nations have claimed sovereignty in the airspace over their home or occupied landmasses, and over water to distances appropriate to seaborne threats, or the adjacency of neighbouring claims. In the early days of the century, if a nation's airspace was threatened, leather-clad pilots would check their gun-breech mechanisms, climb into their fabric-covered biplanes, start the engine and roar-off from small grass fields on missions full of uncertainty and perils.

Attacks could arrive at anytime of the day, so at sun-up the first defenders would be flying over the misty, rose-tinted scenery. This was the legendary dawn patrol. Defending fighter pilots would hold formation defying the icy wind and propellor slipstream in their faces.

Romantics may often wish that those days were back, but the old-timers have left tales which paint the picture more honestly. There were long spells of boredom, as the majority of missions ended without an engagement. But when an attack did take place, it was always the one who saw the other first who had the upper hand. Attackers tried to force a dog-fight by diving from above, and if it was late enough in the day they would race out of the sun's glare, taking advantage of speed and surprise. Most frustrating of all to the pilots who flew the dawn patrol however, was when the enemy sneaked in, left a few holes somewhere behind their own lines, and sneaked out again without being detected.

In the First World War the solution was to put up as many patrols as possible, and then, when the quarry was hunted down, the fights were spectacular. A few wheeling dog-fighters would soon draw the attention of others around, until the sky was filled with the cacophony of the aerial battle. Infantrymen, locked in muddy trenches often marvelled at their compatriots as they swerved, looped and weaved about between bursts of gunfire, and cheered if they were fortunate enough to see a 'kill'.

In the Second World War dawn patrols were a little bit different. They still took place, but by now the aircraft were sleek monoplanes, their

A Nieuport Scout pilot prepares to take-off on a patrol from St Omer in December 1917

When a dogfight was reported by land-line, squadrons would be mobilised to join in the mellee. These Bristol Fighters scrambled from Serny aerodrome in June 1918

LEFT A British RE.8 returns to an aerodrome near Arras in February 1918, at the end of a dawn patrol

pilots were enclosed and in radio contact with the ground and each other. They had armaments which could fill large volumes of sky with lethal concentrations of gunfire, and aids to assist in aiming the same. The biggest difference was that radar stations had assured defenders of early detection of their adversaries. When attackers (British or German) realised that radar-directed retaliation was too much to bear they resorted to night-bombing, and by late-1940 many of the threats that had made the dawn patrol worthwhile had been eliminated through the application of ground-based radar systems.

However, a new form of attack developed. On still mornings hit-and-run raiders could creep in at very low altitudes. They were called hedgehoppers. Radar, which cannot see low-altitude targets, due to the curvature of the earth, were useless against such threats. The attackers would pounce on their targets while the air was still and clear, and the defensive system was shaking off

the effects of the previous night. Radar might have diminished the need for a dawn patrol, but with threats like this around it had hardly abolished it.

Even during the 1940's therefore, defenders would rise like their legendary forebears, over expanses of mirror-flat water, above valleys in which mists drifted as lightly as feathers on the morning air currents, and across towns where factory chimneys were belching coils of smoke in preparation for a day of labour. Radio calls would alert crews of enemy raids, usually very late, but then it was better late than never. Men and their machines would roar down from altitude, converting potential energy to speed as they raced in pursuit of the slick raiders. If they caught sight of several bombers, it was 'tail-end-Charlie', the last man in the formation who had to fight back hardest. After a while it was appreciated that traditional bombers could not mingle with fighters in this sort of battle, and as the war years rolled on there emerged lighter bombers, many of which could outrun contemporary fighters. If cornered they were nimble enough to keep out of those crucifying hails of gunfire.

Then, gradually, over a period of forty years or so, man learned how to use radars which could look down on everything, and see low-flying air-

RAF No. 1 squadron Hurricane crews run to their aircraft after a scramble call

LEFT Hurricanes are seen here in a classical combat formation, with four sets of leaders and wingmen, as they transit a patrol region

TOP LEFT Britain and Germany began to use high-speed, light bombers to attack well-defended targets, and flew below radar coverage. The RAF used the de Havilland Mosquito

LEFT The first service to put AEW into service was the US Navy, and its mainstay today is the Grumman E-2C Hawkeye. Although specifically designed for carrier operations it is also used from shore bases

RIGHT British Aerospace AEW Nimrod has taken on the Royal Air Force roles once attributed to Brisfits and Hurricanes

BELOW A US Air Force Boeing E-3 Sentry crew has a pre-flight discussion before taking off on a modern-day dawn patrol

craft, at whatever height, and at unprecedented ranges. These are the eyes of modern airborne-early warning (AEW) aircraft and they have abolished the need for a dawn patrol.

Even so, fighters still go up and cruise around, on so called combat air patrols, but they do it for rather different reasons nowadays. They are nowhere near so opportunist in their operations. Their movements are monitored by the AEW aircraft, intercepts are controlled and the 'kill', if it occurs at all, can be at such long-range that neither combatant will necessarily see each other. Missiles have replaced hails of bullets.

AEW aircraft growl into the air from aircraft-carriers, or surge down runways on dozens of airbases worldwide. They can be called upon at any hour of the night or day, and on duty they sit for hours near the stratosphere, probing millions of cubic miles of airspace with their electronic eyes and ears. When necessary their duties are relieved only momentarily to drink fuel from a passing tanker. Their crews have to be prepared to be in the air for up to a whole day.

Today some 250 aircraft are used in this way, yet only four types are in service in significant numbers. They include a twin-engined turbo-prop type designed specifically for the job, and three types of revamped airliners, extensively re-equipped with many tons of electronics in place of relaxed multitudes of passengers.

Placing AEW in perspective against other types is not an easy task, because they are few in number and neither nimble nor sleek. Con-

Taxying-out. This is the leisurely bit. Boeing E-3 Sentry
operations can sometimes last for almost 24 hours,
especially when in-flight refuelling is used for extended
patrols, or to ferry aircraft abroad

Airborne. Except for the tell-tale radome above the rear
fuselage this US Air Force E-3 could be just another Boeing
707 flying with one of the world's airlines

sider a good who-dunnit story or a romantic
novel: there may be characters who lurk almost
forgotten and then emerge just a few pages from
the end as the notorious murderer or the myster-
ious lover. AEW aircraft are equivalently enigmatic; they rarely invite more than a passing
mention in most aviation books, so their real
character is rarely discovered. But once stumbled
on they can never be ignored again. For anyone
who has ever wanted to believe that the AEW role
is a passing phase, the pages that follow will
undoubtedly be packed with surprises. They
have become so important that one has to marvel
that the world managed so long with just rudimentary examples. Today they are extremely
sophisticated.

One aim of this book is to defuse the mysteries
of that sophistication. Describing a bow and ar-
row to a stone-age man, whose greatest fighting
asset was a club or a chunk of rock, would have
been a daunting enough task; but he had to know,
or face death under a hail of sharp missiles.
Understanding modern electronic systems falls
into a similar category, as without them military
life would hardly be the way it is, but unravelling

Cruising. A US Air Force Boeing E-3 Sentry maintains a watch from over 30,000 ft, its radar keeping an eye on activities in all directions, including where the sun blots out normal vision

their intricacies can take a lot of unexpected turns for those who have never had reason to be involved with them. If radars, computers and communication systems, hemmed-in by their frightening jargon have made AEW seem a less than appealing subject before, the tale which unfolds in these pages will hopefully show that there has been good reason for all the wizardry that has come to stay. Armed with knowledge of why they are there, AEW systems should be less enigmatic than before. Indeed, AEW types are revealed as amongst the most potent of all modern warplanes. Far from being luxuries they are often necessities and their absence can leave areas of weakness. It happened to Britain in 1982, and the lessons learned tragically, but in military terms

very lightly, during the Falklands campaign, are an integral part of the AEW story.

It is unlikely that AEW aircraft will ever be so numerous that they will be amongst the most well-known types, but they have certainly become bizarre and eye-catching, and they are industrious. They patrol 24 hours per day. They are up there, even in peacetime, in strategic parts of the world, when the nostalgic dawn patrol would have been mounted in days of old. In Western Europe and parts of the Continental US, if each home had a light which blinked every time an AEW radar beam swept by, everyone would get used to seeing their rooms illuminated every few seconds. AEW aircraft are that active, and although they are not armed to attack an enemy as such, their deterence value makes them very important to military equilibrium worldwide.

Dawn patrol in the 1980s. A Boeing E-3 Sentry cruises over sea and islands on its peacekeeping mission

Chapter 2
Long-Range Eyes

Early-warning had been a high-priority task for armies and navies even before the age of the aeroplane, but it was not until man could get above terrain, or that most natural of all hiding phenomena, the curvature of the earth, that truly long-range detection of threats, was possible.

Airborne-early warning was first practiced from balloons. The British Army had much to do with notable early work, and they used tethered balloons which were hauled up 2000 ft or more, carrying a binocular-equipped observer. The spotter would look out for enemy movements, or signal back to artillery officers information on the accuracy of their firing. Although they provided only limited surveillance, the technique was often very advantageous, and armies throughout the world designed and produced their own spotter balloons. In the UK this work was conducted with official backing at the Royal Balloon Factory, on Laffan's Plain west of the town of Farnborough, Hampshire. Small airships also featured in development programmes until the aeroplane established its supremacy.

A rather bright fellow whose flambuoyant background had caused him to experiment with man-carrying kites, though initially as a public stunt, was one William Cody. Around the turn of the century he obtained official sponsorship from the military and moved into Farnborough with a string of kites on a single tethered cable, which would support a basket large enough to carry an observer aloft in weather conditions which would have unacceptably buffeted a balloon. The idea was therefore complementary to tethered balloons, and it promised to pave the way for aerial spotting to be conducted on more occasions.

Aircraft overtook both the balloon and kite rather rapidly however. Indeed, it was Cody who made a place for himself in British aviation history by becoming the nation's first aviator. He made hops across the open heath on Laffan's Plain, the place which today is familiar biennially to the world aviation community during the Farnborough air show. In between time the buildings on the airfield have progressed from being the Royal Balloon Factory, via Royal Aircraft Factory to the Royal Aircraft Establishment. It has been Britain's leading government-run research centre throughout the history of aviation, and contributions by it and its associated establishments appear frequently in the tale of British airborne-early warning developments.

Europe was the birthplace of aviation warfare, events causing air forces to spring rapidly from fledging to full armed-service status during the First World War. It is worth remembering that many of these forces started life as mere limbs of the army, dedicated to spotter duties, and their first aircraft were often tailor-made for the task. They soon carried guns, but were then out-gunned or out manoeuvred when the purpose-built fighter came along, attempting to assert what is all too nonchalantly termed 'air-superiority' in modern warfare.

Only towards the back end of the First World War did bombers begin to operate in earnest, most earlier offensive operations having been conducted by spotter or fighter-types adapted to carry very small payloads. The lack of reliable records of the results from these rather piecemeal operations did much to champion the case for more effective air-to-ground reconnaissance, and therefore photo-reconnaissance became an important role at an early age in aviation history. Equally as important was the task of photographing enemy activities.

Aerial photography has been traced back to October 1858 when a Frenchman, Paul Nadar, photographed Paris from a balloon. Many examples of photographs taken from captive and free-floating balloons exist from the late nineteenth century. Given that photography itself dates from the same period, the rapid development of aerial photography is a strong testimony to the value of this new form of reconnaissance.

If one wants information on the dynamic state of whatever is being observed, it is necessary to take photographs at several times, and to either interpolate or extrapolate observable trends. This takes time, and in many cases it takes too long. Photo-reconnaissance has also always been a dangerous task, for as air-superiority concepts have hardened, the ability to detect and destroy aircraft trying to penetrate defences has increased enormously. This recording technique is hardly out-of date however, and its complementary usefulness to airborne early-warning will perhaps be clearer when radar capabilities have been looked at in detail. Photo-reconnaissance made commander's familiar with being

The first aerial spotters used by the military services were Army observers who ascended beneath specially-built balloons. This example was preparing for an ascent to observe artillery fire in 1916

Observers on duty in balloons were easy prey for early fighters, and a wilting balloon, riddled with machine-gun fire, is seen here shortly before . . .

. . . highly flammable hydrogen gas content ignited and caused the observer's basket to crash to the ground. Army observers used parachutes before airmen—for fairly obvious reasons

able to take in details on a large-scale, yet although it provided excellent records of particular details, it was hardly able to detect and identify aircraft flying in the camera's field-of-view. Radar is much better suited to the latter task.

Radar was born in Europe, where the historical intransigence of nations has fermented more bloodshed than can ever have been justified to maintain territorial gains. The stimulus to seek a form of surveillance which would detect moving objects existed even before the Second World War, and both Britain and Germany had recognized the feasibility of radar. While it is customary to claim that radar was invented in Britain by Watson-Watt and scientific civil service colleagues around 1936, one has to give due consideration in any review of radar development that they were the first team to truly grasp the potential of 'radio-direction and ranging' (radar) techniques. Patents for devices operating on the same principle had been lodged since the turn of the century, and more often than not in countries such as Denmark and Germany, but a successful demonstration had not occurred.

Gun-ranging radars had been successfully developed before 1939 by German engineers, but their ambitions were frustrated by the lack of a readily-available source of sufficient short-wave-

SE.5A Royal Air Force pilots of 85 squadron pose in their SE.5As at St. Omer in June 1918. Patrols by squadrons like this superseded observation balloons on enemy-aircraft detection duties

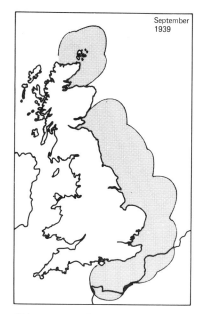

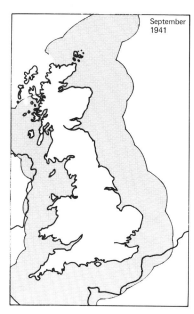

CH coverage diagrams
British CH ground-based radars were used for the first comprehensive early-warning system in the world. The coverage was extended during the early part of the Second World War, detection of intruders flying at 15,000 ft being possible over the areas shown in these diagrams

length or 'microwave' energy. However, Britain had recognised the potential to emit pulses of fairly long-wavelength radiation, and to determine airborne target distances by measuring the time delay between pulse transmission and reception. Initially, these large ground radar were unsteerable, and such bearing information as was available was of relatively poor quality.

Progress with ground-based systems was rapid. By 3 September 1939, when Britain entered the Second World War, the Royal Air Force had 20 Chain Home (CH) radar stations operational. These were on coastal sites which provided coverage out to sea from the Orkney Islands in the north, down the east coast (there was a gap near Petershead which was filled by September 1940), and along the south coast to the Isle of Wight. By September 1940 expansion of this system had extended coverage along the south coast to Lands End, and within a further year there was coverage up the west coast too, almost encircling England, Scotland and Wales.

Most sites used two towers, either 76 m (250 ft) or 107 m (350 ft) tall, and had 200 kW transmitters which produced radiation at between 10 and 13.5 m wavelength (30 to 22 MHz frequency). The antenna was a wire array hung between the towers. Some stations had a second radar, called Chain-Home Low (CHL), which was a shorter wavelength set, operating around 1.5 m wavelength (200 MHz) and derived from gun-laying radar experience. Each of these sets had a smaller, rotating antenna on top

of a mast about 61 m (200 ft) high, and was especially developed to detect low-flying aircraft. Direction-finding accuracy was very good with CHL, which emitted two overlapping beams and measured the relative signal strength of returning energy. It is a technique called monopulse today, but it has little further relevance to the AEW story. In general, the British radars were limited by the long wavelengths used. Nevertheless, they were powerful units and a CH station, in favourable conditions, could see aircraft approaching at 5000 ft over 40 nm away, and at 30,000 ft they were visible 140 nm away.

Independently, German scientists had developed the Freya and Würzburg radars. Their configurations are recognisable as forerunners of modern installations. Freya was similar to CHL, using 2.5 m wavelength (120 MHz) signals radiated from a rotating mesh antenna at ground level. Würzburg was a 50 cm wavelength (600 MHz) radar, which again had a small ground-level antenna, this time a paraboloid dish. Its secrets were revealed to UK scientists after a daring raid on a coastal radar site at Cap d'Antifer, near Bruneval in Britany, during the night of 27–28 March, 1942.

In both nations these radars were the predecessors of airborne-interception (AI) systems fitted to night fighters. The RAF made the most notable progress, having AI Mk II installed in Beaufighters and Blenheims by the time that war was declared. These used 1.5 m wavelength (200 MHz frequency) radiation and were related

Aircraft detection took to the electronic era in the late-1930s when Britain built a chain of radar stations along its coast. The three towers on the left of this photograph comprised a typical Chain Home (CH) radar installation

Often 300 ft-high, the CH radar station towers were easy landmarks. They were difficult to hit however, as such small targets had to be dive-bombed, and they detected the high-flying attackers many miles away

to the CHL installations. The antenna was a fixed aerial which was below the outer wing section. Royal Navy Fairey Swordfish torpedo-bombers had the same sets, slightly modified, and installed to assist in the detection of submarines on the surface at night. The antenna was mounted on the interplane struts and was possibly the only airborne-radar installation put into production for a biplane. Anti-submarine radar development later took on its own complexion, and is as fascinating a tale as AEW development itself.

As might be expected German and British scientists had produced radars which could warn ships of approaching aircraft. The Germans used 50 cm wavelength sets, similar to the Bruneval Würzburg, but with a mesh antenna which was installed on the highest part of the ship. The first British-built 7 m wavelength (45 MHz) surveillance radars were installed on HMS *Rodney* and HMS *Sheffield* in the summer of 1938. Britain also developed 50 cm gun-laying radars, includ-

ing the Type 282 for anti-aircraft use, Type 283 for long-range heavy-barrage and anti-aircraft use, and the Type 284 for surface-gunnery ranging. HMS *Sheffield* had an early Type 284 and used the equipment to shadow the German battleship *Bismarck* in 1941. The British ship's name appears again, even more intimately involved with the AEW story, forty-one years later.

All the above developments were to become little more than mere foundations however. The story of microwave (3 to 10 cm wavelength) radar was the starting point for the most promising radar developments, providing effective airborne systems during the later war years.

In February 1940, at Birmingham University, Prof J. T. Randall and A. H. Boot, following intuition and some promising discoveries in recent research, experimented with a large copper anode into which was sculptured a cavity enclosing a central cathode. Electrical charges passed through the device in the presence of electrical and magnetic fields resonated at microwave frequencies in the gap between cathode and anode, and the device immediately became known as a magnetron. It was almost totally a result of practical development, had little theoretical basis for its operation, and was only just efficient enough to make it worthwhile. But it was a tremendous breakthrough, and its subsequent development has had more than a mere passing influence on the shaping of aeronautical history. As much as any other proud boast by British scientists about the 'firsts' which they can claim, this ranks as one that was especially remarkable. It was what Germany had needed all along, and one could pontificate indefinitely about how different the terrible conflict that raged between 1939–1945 would have been if the magnetron principle had been first discovered in Germany.

Within a year the magnetron was in production. Its use was accelerated by a technical exchange of information which saw America introduced to the new device, and UK engineers presented with a lot of useful information on US microwave-antenna technology, which like Germany's was languishing without a sufficiently powerful source of energy.

A magnetron-based radar was carried aloft for the first time in a Blenheim from Christchurch, near Bournemouth, in March 1941, and although subsequently developed in many stages this was the first set with the H₂S designation. This unusual title has been often attributed to the fact that the radar set produced a stink like rotten eggs, ie. hydrogen sulphide, which has the chemical symbol H_2S, but it is a highly unlikely tale. A more plausible story is that when crews were eventually allowed to fly magnetron-based radars over enemy territory, they were told that should they be taken prisoner they would claim it was wiring for a system yet to be installed which was designed to help them find their way back to base. The radar was henced dubbed 'home, sweet, home.'

If radar could detect enemy activity, such as aircraft movements, it was an obvious advance on photo-reconnaissance techniques, not least because it could present a dynamic picture of events as they happened. This took a long time to perfect (about three decades before airborne-early warning was thoroughly reliable at long ranges). It has taken the best of modern electronic technology to achieve the desired end-point, and brought tremendous change in the techniques of airborne interdiction.

Before delving into the use of an airborne-surveillance post, one further associated activity must be considered to outline the broadest possible view of AEW activities. Aircraft are not the only man-made objects that pass over our heads. Since October 1957, when the Soviet Sputnik 1 first went into orbit around the earth, more satellites have been pushed into space than even the

A second radar introduced in Britain, around 1940, was the Chain Home Low (CHL) installation. This comprised a small rotating antenna on a 200 ft-high tower, and being a higher frequency set it was better than CH at detecting low-level intruders

British radar-equipped fighters pioneered airborne radar operations in secret, and although useful the radar was nowhere near as effective as the public was later told. This Beaufighter has an AI IV installation, and the crew were apparently successful at shooting down enemy aircraft

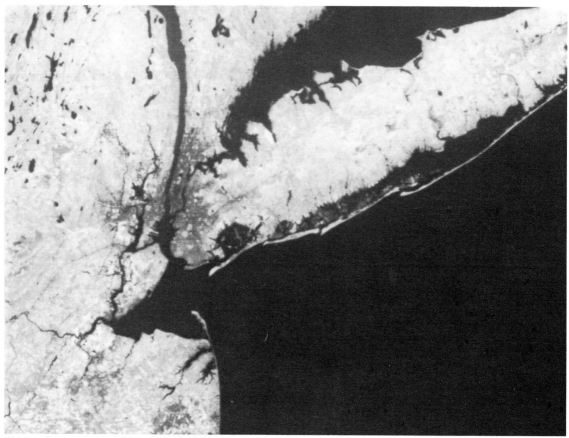

This Landsat's eye-view of New York City alludes to the
high-resolution performance of spy satellites

most sincere devotee could have contemplated in
those early days.

Space is vastly different from the atmosphere
for a reason which has nothing at all to do with
any of the physical attributes that characterise
gaseous mixtures or a virtual vacuum. Officially,
space is politically neutral. The territorial boundaries that nation's have set up on the Earth's
surface, and found good excuse to extend
upwards into the airspace (and out to sea) do not
exist in space. It would be pointless to insist that
they did, for any orbiting body describes a well
defined path, rotating once about the earth at a
regular interval which is roughly proportional to
the satellite's distance from the centre of the
earth. One can no more keep an orbiting spacecraft in a particular patch of space than one can
stop the moon from continuously passing overhead various territorial areas. It was a practical
move to declare space as stateless, but to believe
it is also politically neutral is somewhat naive.

Once man had demonstrated that from his arti-
ficial satellites he could photograph the weather,
or thermally-image agricultural areas and the
oceans to detect crop diseases and ocean currents

on scales hitherto unimaginable, it was clear that
spy-satellites would be up there too. Compared
to aircraft operations, the altitudes are vast.

Any survey of the number of satellites orbitted,
and a breakdown of the civil/military proportions
soon reveals how active the defence departments
of the superpowers are, and one must infer that
many of the military payloads are spy satellites,
if for no other reason than that neither country
is willing to talk about them. We know now that,
although not officially acknowledged by either
side, there are photographic satellites in space
which can detect objects as small as 30 cm (1 ft)
across. That is to say, a black cast-iron manhole
cover on a concrete runway could appear on a
photographic image from a satellite. This technology has reached the point where it is accepted
that when a major conflict arises the superpowers
will put up special satellites, or change existing
satellite orbits, to monitor what is going on:
events in the Middle East and the Falkland
Islands have been the kind of occasions that have
demonstrated the fact clearly. America uses the
Big Bird and KH-11 satellites, the latter virtually
in permanent stand-by to be manoeuvred wher-

The Space Shuttle is an invaluable anti-satellite/reconnaissance asset

ever, and whenever desired, and beaming details of what it sees back to the US on a microwave link. The Soviets often eject capsules which contain film, and which can be processed rapidly after recovery, to provide high quality pictures.

A natural further development would be to use space-based radar, and in this respect the Soviets seem to have grasped the nettle firmly. Trying to view small objects at great ranges with radar calls for large aerials, but the bonus from such a system is that it is a very accurate all-weather surveillance system. Often three radars are placed in similar orbits to give almost continuous coverage of large areas of the earth's surface. Like with any radar, the system's pulses can be detected in the area which it illuminates, so a fleet of ships which might know they are shielded from prying satellite cameras by cloud cover can usually tell if they are being watched by Soviet-satellite radars. The Americans, it is believed, have placed greater emphasis on eaves-dropping. Their passive satellites are undetectable, but they can pin-point the location of ground transmitters, and gather valuable electronic intelligence.

Spacecraft experts are now declaring that the

statelessness of space is mythical, and in the US there is a strong lobby which claims that Soviet killer-satellites are already in orbit. These can be packed with explosives (conventional or thermonuclear), and are manoeuvrable. On reaching the vicinity of a target satellite they can eject warheads to destroy it, explode alongside, or direct a hugely-powerful laser at the target, rapidly delivering so much energy into a tiny area that the target either burns away or explodes immediately. The US is developing space-based laser weapons to counteract such threats.

This sort of warfare, although it might seem far removed, has a lot to do with airborne-early warning. If space is such an unsafe place to put your billion-dollar snoopers, then it is logical to develop equally effective units which can be protected in airspace over which you have control. The radar is also closer to the objects of interest, so it does not have to be quite so powerful, the system has greater operational flexibility as it is not being whirled around an enormous orbit, and one can have men with the sensor who are able to send out commands which ensure that ground, sea and airborne forces respond rapidly and in a co-ordinated manner to threats detected by the airborne surveillance-post. These features are the keys to airborne-early warning effectiveness, and were the aircraft and their systems not so complex, and therefore expensive, airborne-early warning aircraft would undoubtedly be on every air force's shopping list.

It is clear that when the full value of modern radar and associated sensor technology is realised, and command, control and communication (C^3) capabilities are available less expensively, these rare aircraft will begin to assume a dramatic importance. The required technology is well within the grasp of the major industrial nations, and the US, UK and Soviet Union all have airborne early-warning aircraft in service. The Nato consortium, and countries such as Israel, Japan, Saudi Arabia, Egypt and Singapore, who feel it is necessary to have such aircraft themselves, have purchased systems, in every case from the US, and by the time this book is published it seems certain that France will also have decided to purchase or develop an AEW capability. Of the major AEW types in service today, just one was in use in the early sixties, and most have been produced since 1975. Yet by 1985 a worldwide fleet of 250 or so aircraft will exist. Along sensitive borders there will be almost continuous airborne surveillance from aircraft which more than any others have earned the reputation of being 'eyes in the sky.'

Chapter 3
AEW Radar Technology

When the serious matter of how other aircraft movements are detected and monitored, individual movements identified and tracked, and eventually detected or destroyed, radar will be revealed to be just one system used. It is however the most complex of all the sensors in an AEW aircraft, and the development of advanced airborne radars is what has made AEW aircraft a viable proposition. An understanding of the technology involved is highly desirable therefore, and as AEW aircraft tend to use the most advanced and most powerful airborne radars in production, it has been necessary to devote a chapter to describing their characteristic.

This is an introductory description for all categories of airborne-early warning radars. It tries to steer clear of expressions peculiar to radar engineers, and summaries are presented with illustrations.

Radar principles

Searchlights and radars have several common features. Both emit electromagnetic radiation—in one case it is visible, in the other case it is not—and the receiver looks for evidence of reflected radiation. Radar provides its own form of illumination, and has to combine both transmission and reception elements. In all AEW radars, and as in most other radar types, these two components use a common viewing element, which is called the antenna.

The three radar components identified already (antenna, transmitter and receiver) are linked by a fourth element, the duplexer. This is a relatively simple device, and as it has little influence on target-detection performance its detail does not need to concern the reader.

Whereas a searchlight illuminates continuously, a radar has to illuminate briefly, then remain alert for evidence of returning radiation. A pulse of radar energy is emitted therefore, and a time interval reserved for the receiver to listen. The number of pulses emitted each second is called the pulse repetition frequency (PRF), and how many pulses per second a system emits decides whether it is a low, medium or high PRF

set. It will be seen later that the category, in this respect, is vitally important to understanding how the receiver works.

A common feature of all radars has been seen to be the transmission of pulses, and the reception of pulse echoes. Some idea of how weak these echoes can be will provide an insight into the scale of transmitter and receiver design objectives.

Radiation spreads out from a radar set, approximately such that the area illuminated by any pulse increases in proportion to the square of the distance from the radar set. Due to this effect, tripling the range to a given-size target reduces the power striking it by nine times. By quadrupling the distance, power reaching it is reduced by 16 times, and so on.

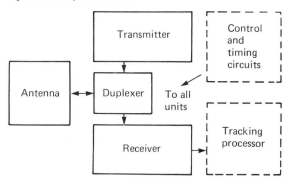

Radar components
All AEW Radars use a single antenna which, via a duplexer unit, is linked to transmitter and receiver systems. The technology used in these components is considered in detail in this chapter. Additionally there are control and timing circuits, and a tracking processor. The latter function is handled in the main processor of AEW types

On being reflected back, the radiation goes through exactly the same process, so tripling the range to any target means that the returning energy will be reduced by a factor of $9 \times 9 (=81)$, and quadrupling the distance it will be reduced by a factor of $16 \times 16 (=256)$.

This means that, for a given receiver sensitivity, and antenna size, the maximum radar-detection range is proportional to the fourth-root of transmitted power, so for long-range operations, in addition to using an extremely high power transmitter, it is desirable that the radar receiver is very sensitive, and that the antenna is as large as possible.

To give some feel for the operation of a typical radar, consider the example of a radar transmitter which produces, on average, 10 kW power output, and emits pulses which are 1/50,000th second duration, every 1/500th of a second. The radar is transmitting for only one per cent of the time available, so the peak power output is equivalent to 1 MW. This is the sort of peak power output that a long-range radar needs.

In the same example, there is roughly 1/500th of a second for the receiver to listen for echoes, and the maximum range from which an echo could return before the next pulse was emitted, would be about 300 km. On low-PRF radars this is the way that maximum operating range is defined, but later in this chapter, when medium-PRF and high-PRF operations are considered, this limitation will be overruled.

A further leading influence on the design of a radar transmitter is that the radar designer might accord high priority to the ability to change the radar frequency occasionally, if only to complicate the task of an enemy trying to blot out the radar system by blinding it with radiation of a similar wavelength. The act of blinding radars in this way is called 'jamming,' and is a topic returned to occasionally in later chapters. The technique of avoiding jamming by changing the radar frequency is called frequency-agility.

Sufficient guidance has been provided now to appreciate the range of performance objectives which face a radar designer, and to look at the major types of radar antennas, transmitters and receivers in everyday use.

Radar antennas

First, recall that a radar antenna is designed to produce a concentrated beam of energy, directed outwards with as little divergence as possible. It has also to work in reverse, collecting radar energy and concentrating it for the receiver. The emphasis on directivity is one reason why the most suitable radar antenna has to be chosen carefully.

There is also the question of the radar's operating wavelength. In the introduction there was cause to comment on how the first British radars, used to detect approaching bomber and fighter swarms, were soon complemented with very-short wavelength radars which used the magnetron. These examples tend to bracket the full range of wavelengths used in radars, from as high as 50 m when a long-range ground installation is used (although such long wavelengths are used rarely nowadays) to as little as a few centimetres for some airborne systems. The shortest wavelengths (3 cm or less) tend to be attenuated and reflected by rain, and are therefore especially suitable for weather radars, but they are consequently of little value to the airborne early-warning radar designer. He has to use longer wavelengths, and around 10 cm wavelength radiation is used in most systems, although units operating around 70 cm are still in service. Armed with this meagre knowledge it is possible to consider the pros and cons of the leading antenna types.

Paraboloid (dish) antenna

When a searchlight reflector focusses light into a dazzling beam, it is operating very efficiently. This is largely because the reflector is many millions of times larger than the wavelength of light, and in this case reflections from a paraboloid shaped surface will obey the simple laws of reflections which are taught in schools. Even so, a parallel-sided beam is not achieved, and the beams of light always spread slightly with distance. The same is true if a dish is used to reflect radar waves, so the paraboloid dish, although used extensively in early AEW systems, is nowadays regarded as a poor performer. Its use in AEW systems has been limited to the simplest applications.

The paraboloid dish antenna was widely used until the early 1960s, since when its usefulness has diminished. This example is used in the Ferranti Seaspray radar for the Westland Lynx helicopter

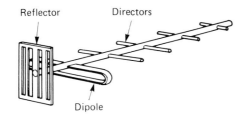

Yagi antenna
The yagi antenna is not widely associated with aircraft radars nowadays, although it was used a lot on early long-wavelength sets. It is of interest in AEW applications because the Grumman E-2 Hawkeye still has this type of antenna in its rotodome

Yagi antenna

This is the most familiar of all household TV-set aerials comprising a rod with roughly regularly-spaced bars, which although greatly appreciated by ornithological species, were not deliberately designed to be comfortable perches.

The elements of Yagi antenna, named after a Japanese scientist, include a dipole, where radiation is transmitted and received, and adjacent to it a reflector, plus extra elements strung-out in the direction along which radiation is to be transmitted or received.

The distance between the dipole and the reflector should be about one-half of the wavelength of radiation being used, and the antenna elements are spaced at a slightly smaller interval. The more extra elements, called directors, are included, the more directivity will be achieved. Several Yagi antennas can be linked to form an array, and this technique is used successfully in the Grumman E-2 Hawkeye radar. In more recent AEW installations the Yagi antenna has been superseded. It is unique in being an antenna which obtains its directivity and sensitivity from its length rather than its breadth.

Slotted waveguide/phased-array

First, it is important to appreciate that radar energy can be piped, rather like a fluid. If the pipe is not of exactly the right cross-section, or the correct linear dimension, and its bends do not conform to precise formulae, the energy losses can be very significant. This form of radiation-ducting is called a waveguide. It is usually of rectangular section, at least 2 cm (0.8 in) or so on each side, and may be several times larger, depending on the wavelength of the radiation carried.

Slotted-waveguide antennas, as the name implies, are an extension of the waveguide with slots cut in the faces. Basically, the waveguide is folded several times to form a large outward-facing area into which slots are cut to precise dimensions, at regular intervals, and at specific places in the waveguide wall. The geometry of the waveguide shaping and the relative locations and dimensions of the slots have to be defined with

This is the Westinghouse AN/APY-2 radar antenna for the Boeing E-3 Sentry. Essentially it is a slotted-waveguide type, but it also has phase-shifters, not visible here, which provide some phased-array characteristics

tremendous precision. If the calculations are carried out correctly and the antenna is the right shape, a highly directional beam is produced. This antenna is widely used and is found in the Boeing E-3 Sentry radar.

The phased-array antenna, like the slotted-waveguide type, has many individual radiating elements in a single installation.

The main point about the phased-array antenna is that the phase of signals into (and out

The Boeing E-3 Sentry rotodome consists of an elliptically-shaped centre, onto which antennas are attached, and two black semi-circular planform radomes to streamline the assembly

Phased-array techniques are used in the Boeing E-3 radar to stabilize the beam in the vertical plane. This is called a two-dimensional phased-array antenna. The photograph above shows a three-dimensional, or 'fully' phased-array antenna, which has no moving parts. The equipment shown is an electronically-agile radar (EAR) test set developed by Westinghouse in the US

of) each element or group of elements, can be individually adjusted by 'phase shifters' to produce a desired radiation pattern, or combination of patterns, pointing in the desired direction (or directions). This means that one radar antenna can be extremely versitile.

In the past, phased-array antennas, which are popular now for large ground-based radars, have been regarded as too heavy for airborne use, but a miniaturised phased-array antenna has been flown in a B-52, and the technology has been adopted for the Rockwell B-1B strategic bomber. The slotted-waveguide antenna used in the Boeing E-3 Sentry also uses phase-shifters to adjust the elevation of the emitted radiation, stabilising the pattern when the aircraft is banking. They can also scan it to determine target elevation.

Because of the precise radiation-pointing control and easy scanning abilities of the fully phased-array antenna, plus its ability in some instances to provide more powerful pulses than a

waveguide-fed antenna, this antenna design is likely to be a strong favourite for future AEW system designs.

Inverted-cassegrain antenna

This is probably the least easy to understand of all radar antennas. In all inverted-cassegrain designs the transmitter radiation is emitted from a waveguide at the centre of a forward-facing main reflector, which can be a flat-plate or paraboloid-shaped dish. The radiation is bounced off a smaller rear-facing reflector, or sub-dish, therefore turning it towards the larger main-reflector, where after a second turnabout it is emitted into space. When receiving radiation the reverse path is used.

Several types of cassegrain antenna are used, but the only one that need concern us here is that type with a convex hyperboloid sub-dish. In this arrangement, the whole antenna system is swivelled, the waveguide remaining fixed, to direct the radar energy in the required direction. The sub-dish causes aperture blockage (it is like looking ahead with a hand only a few inches from your eyes) so it has to be rendered 'transparent' by a polarisation-twisting scheme. This depends on having a linearly-polarised radiation source, and the principal objective is to reflect the radiation from a sub-dish which is an efficient reflector of waveguide-supplied radiation, but which is transparent to the same radiation when it has been reflected from the main reflector.

Embedded in the sub-dish therefore are many parallel wires. The separation between each wire is critical (it is usually about one-fifth of the radar wavelength), and with the wires set parallel to the plane of linear polarisation of the waveguide

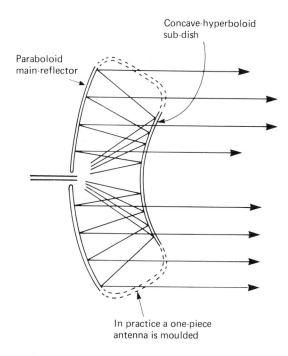

Concave-hyperboloid sub-dish

Paraboloid main-reflector

In practice a one-piece antenna is moulded

Polarisation-twisting
A drawback of the inverted-cassegrain antenna is that the sub-dish blocks forward view from the main-reflector. Polarised radiation is used in all radars, and fortunately it can be twisted as it passes through a cassegrain scanner, by sets of wires in the reflectors. Outgoing radiation is reflected conventionally at the sub-dish, then twisted through 90 degrees at the main-reflector. The sub-dish construction does not affect the reflected radiation due to its different polarisation

Inverted-cassegrain antenna
There are several antenna variations which can be classified as inverted-cassegrain types, of which the paraboloid main-reflector/hyperboloid sub-dish combination shown here is one. This antenna configuration is used in the BAe AEW Nimrod

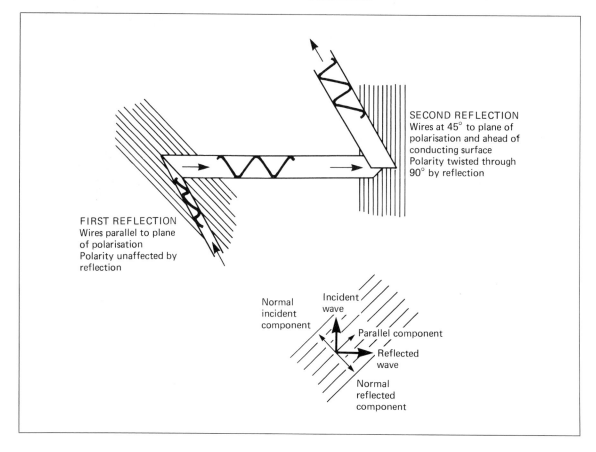

SECOND REFLECTION
Wires at 45° to plane of polarisation and ahead of conducting surface
Polarity twisted through 90° by reflection

FIRST REFLECTION
Wires parallel to plane of polarisation
Polarity unaffected by reflection

Normal incident component

Incident wave

Parallel component

Reflected wave

Normal reflected component

The airborne-interception radar used in Britain's Tornado F.2 uses an inverted-cassegrain antenna

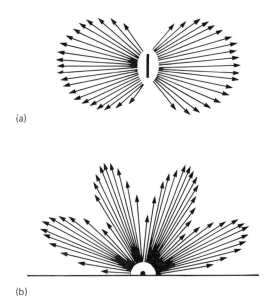

(a)

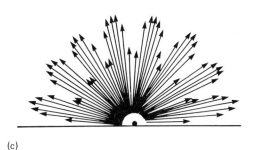

(b)

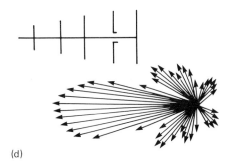

(c)

(d)

(measured relative to the E-field for boffin readers) this arrangement reflects all the radiation with its polarity unchanged. Most importantly, this type of sub-dish is transparent to radiation with its polarity set at 90 degrees to that emitted from the waveguide.

The main reflector which complements the sub-dish therefore has to 'twist' the radiation-polarisation through 90 degrees. To do this it too has many parallel wires embedded. This time they are aligned at 45 degrees to the sub-dish wires, and suspended in a di-electric material so that they are approximately one-quarter of a wavelength distance ahead of a conducting surface. An illustration can provide a more clear description of the way that the polarisation is twisted as it bounces off the main-reflector.

Radiation received in the opposite direction goes through exactly the same process, in reverse, before reaching the receiver.

It has been necessary to look at this complicated system because a twisting inverted-cassegrain type antenna is used in the British AEW Nimrod radar installation. It was attractive to the British designers because it is a relatively small and therefore lightweight antenna which has much less inertia than a slotted-waveguide or phased-array antenna.

Antenna sidelobes

Several times in the description of antenna operation it has been possible to sidetrack the implications of antenna directivity, but an insight into the subject is necessary.

First consider a dipole (single-wire strand) aerial which is emitting electromagnetic energy in space. As shown on an adjacent diagram it radiates in all directions around itself, but hardly

Antenna sidelobes
There is a temptation to believe that radars emit radiation straight ahead, with no scattering about the main direction. This is not the case and these illustrations demonstrate that sidelobes are unavoidable. Figure (a) shows a simple aerial in space. It radiates evenly all round, but not up and down. At figure (b) the same aerial is shown on the ground, and now a distinctly-lobed pattern is

visible. If the length of the antenna is doubled, as shown at figure (c), more lobes are formed. A direct conclusion of this train of illustrations is that radiation lobing is natural and unavoidable. Large antennas are less prone to lobing, and when a directional aerial is used, as in figure (d), a prominent radiation lobe is produced in the desired direction, but small subsidiary lobes are still produced in other directions

at all above and below. A plot of radiation intensity around the aerial looks like a doughnut, with a very small central hole where the dipole is located.

When a dipole is located on the ground the pattern is less simple. It now sets-up a radiation pattern which, in section, is also shown diagramatically in the adjacent set of illustrations. In the first case illustrated the aerial length equals the radiation wavelength, and the second illustration shows that if the wavelength is halved, the radiation pattern looks more complex. Carrying on, decreasing wavelength (or increasing the dipole length would have the same effect), will produce eventually almost equal radiation strength in all directions, although in actual fact the radiation pattern would consist of many tightly-packed lobes.

If a directive aerial is studied. (a Yagi antenna is shown, but it could be any type discussed) it will be found to have a similar lobe-packed radiation pattern, except that radiation in the forward direction will be in the most pronounced lobe. This is called the main beam, and the remainder of the pattern forms what are called sidelobes. There will be plenty of occasions for returning to the subject of sidelobes, as to the radar engineer they are like unwanted relations who never fail to appear at the most inopportune moments.

Note that when a radar is transmitting, energy emitted as sidelobes represents wasted power, and when the antenna is receiving the sidelobes can cause detection of targets well off the centre-line of the antenna. These effects render the radar susceptible to easy detection or interference from high-power jammers. The paraboloid dish and yagi antenna configurations have relatively large sidelobes and are not as good as the slotted-wave-guide, phased-array or inverted-cassegrain antennas.

The sidelobe performance of all the systems used in current AEW types will be subject to some scrutiny at various points in the rest of this book, and it should become clear, gradually, how much importance the radar designer will assign to good sidelobe performance.

Radar transmitters

Radar-transmitter systems comprise many electronic circuits and a powerful high-frequency (microwave) electro-magnetic energy source. The circuits take care of timing and quality control functions. They ensure that pulses of radar energy are produced at the required PRF, with each pulse of the appropriate duration and having all the characteristics of frequency, rise-time,

amplitude and so on that has been specified. These are important tasks, but they do not play an integral part in the radar's actual performance, as does the microwave-energy source. Rather in the way that if an accountant was probing the financial standing of a company, he would largely ignore the invoicing techniques used and concentrate on the balance sheet totals, so in looking at a radar transmitter it is possible to by-pass detail about circuits designed to shape pulses, and to concentrate on the characteristics of a few widely-used microwave-energy sources.

Before embarking on descriptions of how each microwave-generating device works, it must be stressed that the units described here represent only the microwave-energy sources found in air-borne-early warning radars. Solid-state devices are also used nowadays, for example in small weather radars or to feed multi-element phased-array antennas, and even in highway speedtrap radars, but their operation is not presented.

Magnetron

A very simple description of the cavity magnetron (not to be confused with solid-state devices also called magnetrons) was given in the introduction. In effect, it is the radar engineer's equivalent of getting notes out of a milk bottle, simply by blowing over the top. In that case, the air in the milk bottle is made to resonate at a frequency which produces the audible note. In a magnetron the mechanism is a lot more complex, but basically electrons travelling between a central cathode and a surrounding anode are subjected to intense electric and magnetic fields. If steady-state conditions are applied, and the electric field is very strong, the electrons are not able to reach the anode, and they form a cloud around the cathode. If an oscillating electric field is introduced, the electrons break out to the anode in bunches, and it is found that they spiral in the magnetron cavity. By having appropriately shaped recesses in the anode this produces regular bunching, converting the available electric-field energy into high-frequency radiation.

The first 'slot-and-hole' anode design, set-up by Randall and Boot in 1940, produced nearly a kilowatt of 10 cm wavelength radiation in brief pulses. This was staggering at the time, but very soon they had it operating at 10 kW, or about 1000 times as effectively as any thermionic valve then available. In service during 1942–1945 the original cavity magnetron was operated to produce 9 cm wavelength radiation at 25 kW peak power output for one microsecond, about 1000 times per second. Mean power output was 25 W.

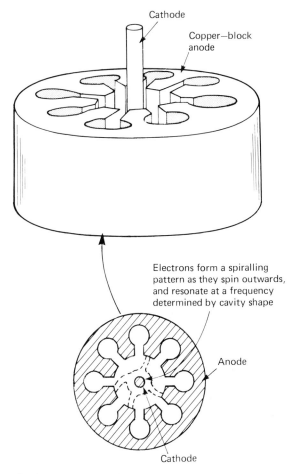

Cathode

Copper—block anode

Electrons form a spiralling pattern as they spin outwards, and resonate at a frequency determined by cavity shape

Anode

Cathode

Cavity magnetron
This was the first efficient method of producing very-short wavelength radiation. It uses an electro magnetic resonance principle by causing electrons which flow from the cathode to rotate at a speed such that in a specially-shaped cavity, achieved by machining the circular anode, resonance occurs at the radar frequency. Although it was widely used in early AEW radars the magnetron is not used in modern sets. It produces a narrow band of wavelengths around the nominal setting, and the phase characteristics from pulse-to-pulse are unpredictable. They are incompatible with pulse-Doppler radar receivers

This magnetron was only a few inches in diameter, and released 70 per cent of the energy put into it as useable radiation. Although magnetrons are important to radars in general, and were used extensively in early systems, they are no longer used in modern AEW radar systems. This is largely because they produce radiation both at and near to the desired frequency, and in random-phase order; attributes which are called non-coherence. They are undesirable features, for reasons which will be more obvious when receiver design is contemplated.

Klystron
The klystron was invented three years before the cavity magnetron and it played a big part in providing experience of using an electron stream to amplify high-frequency signals; an attribute later extended significantly in travelling-wave tubes. It was developed and used as a low-power source of radio energy (longer wavelengths than the microwave energy used by radars) during the Second World War, and by 1949 Stanford University in California had developed a 30MW peak-power klystron which powered its first linear accelerator.

The simplest klystrons have an electron gun at one end of an evacuated tube. From this device a cathode emits a stream of electrons, in exactly the same manner as the electron gun used in television-set cathode-ray tubes, and the stream passes through the centre of a circular cavity. The cavity dimensions are chosen to cause electrons to bunch so that they enter a second or subsequent cavity in bursts, until eventually the electron beam is converted into regular bursts; as one early book on the subject nicely described it—like beads on a necklace. The pulses of amplified high-frequency energy are tapped off.

Klystrons can be very complex and superficially they tend to resemble the coupled-cavity TWT, which is a related device described in more detail below. A joyful attribute for the radar engineer is that the klystron is a coherent device: that is, its main frequency and the phase relationships of pulses can be defined very accurately. One of the most notable current applications of the klystron in an airborne radar is in the Boeing E-3 Sentry radar.

Travelling-wave tubes
Two types of travelling-wave tube (TWT), amongst dozens of possible designs, are used extensively in radars. The original TWT, called the helix-type, is one version. This was invented before the end of the Second World War, and it originally established a strong reputation as a source of microwave radiation for airborne radars.

Around 1963, the coupled-cavity TWT (sometimes called a slow-wave TWT) was developed, and this is used now for many microwave radiation devices, airborne radars included. An important advance introduced subsequently, and applicable to both types of TWT, has been the use of grid-modulation which is essential for efficient operation at high-PRFs.

A helix-type TWT, like a klystron, uses an electron beam directed along a linear tube, but now the beam is directed down the centre of a loosely-wound spiral, which carries the electric field to be amplified. When the beam velocity is approximately equal to the rate of advance of radiation in the spiral, amplification occurs. The amplified microwave energy is tapped from the helix.

Coupled-cavity TWTs are a refinement of the basic design, and instead of using a spiral there are several cavities, each adjacent pair operating rather in the manner of those in a klystron. They are robustly-engineered with the cavities coupled by holes so that resonance is passed along the electron stream. Many electron-amplification cavities can be placed in line, to provide any desired peak power output, although precautions have to be taken to ensure that harmonics are not

also amplified. The development of this TWT type in the mid-1960s represented the zenith of the technology used, and opened many new possibilities to radar designers; but only provided that the TWT could be made to operate at high-PRF settings—between 10,000 and 300,000 pulses per second.

The high-PRF requirement was met successfully by the development of the grid-modulated TWT. Its development was made difficult by the mechanical properties demanded, and although these are largely beaten now, the poor reliability of grid-modulated TWTs was often a bone of contention with radar customers.

The cathode in the electron gun is a heated ele-

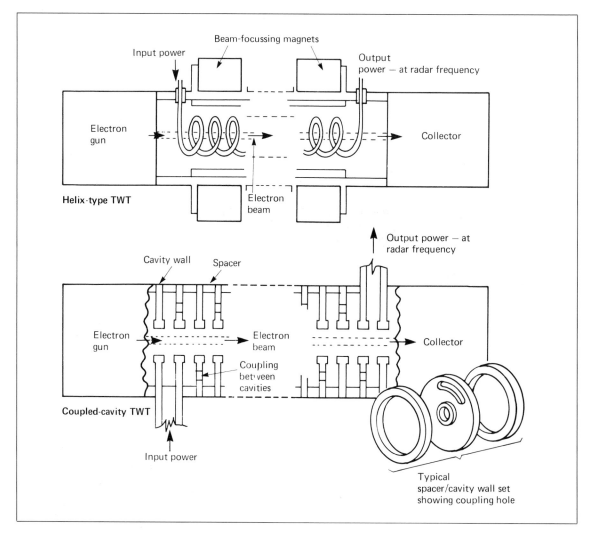

Klystrons/travelling-wave tubes
These related devices have become established at the most suitable source of high-power radar-frequency energy. Both types of TWT in widespread use are shown schematically above, and it is the lower type which is used in several AEW radars. All TWTs have an electron beam passing from an electron gun to a collector. This has the

desired radar-frequency superimposed and induces resonance in energy passing along the helix or cavities. The output is coherent—at one frequency only, and in phase synchronism. In TWTs the frequency can be varied rapidly, from pulse to pulse, in a wide waveband, so TWTs are popular for frequency-agile radars

ment, typically operating above 1100°C, and it has to have a relatively large area to generate sufficient electrons for injections into the TWT. Switching the power supply on and off at the high frequencies demanded is not an efficient method of modulation.

Typically, the cathode is heated to emit continuously and the control grid, which is a foil with many regular-spaced perforations, is suspended just ahead of the cathode face. The grid electric potential is varied to regulate the electron stream emitted by the cathode, but to protect it an intermediate grid, called the shadow grid, is introduced. Usually their is only 0.1 mm separation between the face of the grids, and the cathode surface. Even so, the shadow grid has to be at the same electric potential as the cathode, and although it is bound to reach a very high temperature it must not emit electrons. At the same time neither grid must distort with the temperature changes, nor must their registration be affected by vibration. All-in-all, grid-modulation TWT development was itself a remarkable piece of engineering design. Their commonplace use in modern airborne radars is taken very much for granted, but they were a very essential stepping-stone towards the AEW capability which forms the essential story of this book.

TWTs are used as amplifiers in the Boeing E-3 Sentry radar and as both microwave-energy source and amplifiers in the British AEW Nimrod. TWTs are coherent devices and an attribute that the radar designer is quick to use is that such devices can be operated at any frequency in a relatively wide bandwidth, so the 'frequency-agility' performance is easily achieved.

Radar receivers

This third and final set of notes on radar has a lot to say about the application of modern electronic technology. In simple descriptions of radar the fact that a pulse of reflected energy is detected at an interval after the initial pulse was radiated, and when the beam is aligned in a particular direction, is regarded as justification enough for determining the target range and bearing. Nowadays, a lot more information can be determined too, plus electronic engineers are more adept than ever at recognising what is wanted, and what isn't wanted, so they can, for example, eliminate returns from unwanted objects.

The techniques for doing all this can be given simple names, but these are not always simple or self-evident. It is in this realm where radar engineers often disappear behind a barrage of their own jargon, and it is intended that the myths and legends should be dispelled here. Hence only the relevant details of radar operations need be introduced when actual systems are covered in this book, but the detail is available here for those who crave for a more intimate knowledge of what modern technology is able to achieve.

The statistical nature of receivers

All radar receivers pick up extraneous data. It is random, and amplified it sounds rather like the hiss on a radio which is operating at a high volume setting. Most of this 'noise' comes from within the set, and is therefore unavoidable, but it has one especially significant consequence on actual receiver operation. A target echo must stand out from the background noise, but as a target recedes from the radar the reflected pulse gets smaller, and although it may be theoretically detectable it can be lost in the background noise. The range at which this happens is indistinct and has to be expressed mathematically. Radar engineers will usually quote the *maximum range at which there is a certain probability of detecting a target of a given radar cross-sectional area*. It is important to appreciate that this statistical basis of radar target detection cannot be overcome, and this limitation applies to all types of radar.

Low, medium and high-PRF radars

Fundamental to all pulse radars is the pulse repetition frequency (PRF) which was defined early in this chapter. Until around 1970 all but a few

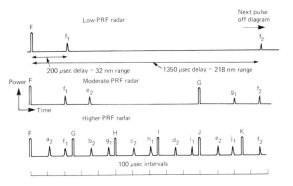

Range-ambiguities in medium/high-PRF radars
Examples of the *timing* diagrams in a set of radars are shown above. The top, low-PRF, illustration shows returns from two targets at 32 and 218 nm. In the moderate-PRF illustration the radar has emitted a second pulse before the response from the most distant target has been received. This causes a 'range-ambiguity' as the receiver does not know that pulse f_2 is not related to pulse G. In the lower diagram the confusion which can arise from only two targets at a higher-PRF is shown. Despite this fundamental drawback, methods of determining unique target-ranges in medium/high-PRF radars have been developed, and are incorporated in all modern AEW sets

airborne radars were what are now categorized as low-PRF sets.

A low-PRF radar is one which has sufficient time between pulses for radiation reflected from a target at the maximum operating range to be received before the next pulse is transmitted. A low-PRF AEW radar which has to view targets at long ranges, perhaps out to 300 km, cannot operate at a PRF in excess of 500 Hz because of this limitation, ie; it takes 1/500th of a second for the radar energy, travelling at the speed of light, to travel out 300 km and back again.

If higher PRFs are used, however, the maximum operating range need not diminish; it is only the maximum range at which range can be measured *unambiguously* that is limited. Medium-PRF radars, emitting several tens of thousands of pulses per second, suffer this 'range-ambiguity' problem.

High-PRF radars, emitting perhaps a hundred thousand or more pulses per second, have what might seem to be enormous range ambiguity problems, but on the other hand their frequency-domain analysis (to be described next) is much easier. The radar designer has to trade-off these two conflicting requirements.

Time-domain and frequency-domain analysis

These two phrases straddle the radar engineer's paradise, and they deserve to be revealed as high-faluting titles which mask innocuous concepts.

'Domain' is used in these two titles in its most literal sense. In essence, information deduced from radar signals by referring to the timing of their arrival (as already described) is 'time-domain' analysis. Referring to the frequency content of the signals received is 'frequency-domain' analysis.

Most newcomers to the radar scene are aware of 'time-domain' analysis. It seems that they expect it, or something like it, and in any case it is easy to associate with many natural sensor functions. Low-PRF radars tend therefore to be easily understood. In medium-PRF radars time-domain analysis is hampered by the range-ambiguity problem, and the resolution of this drawback can require using two or more similar PRFs and sophisticated analysis techniques. It is worthy of note that this sort of work was taken on by early radar engineers. There is nothing startling about the methods, but it was not until the compact airborne digital computer became available that medium and high-PRF radars could become common place. High-PRF radars tend to suffer greater range-ambiguity problems than medium-PRF types and therefore need more capable digital computers.

'Frequency-domain' analysis is often a new field of exploration for non-radar engineers, and as such it deserves to be explained in stages. General guidelines only are presented here.

It is as well to be prepared for what results can be expected when any radar system is frequency

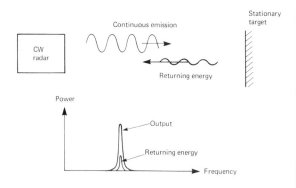

Frequency-domain analysis
An example of a *frequency* diagram is shown above. It relates specifically to a continuous-wave (CW) radar illuminating a stationary object. Weak returning echoes are at the same frequency as radiation emitted. If a frequency search is conducted on all the returning energy therefore, energy is discovered at only one frequency

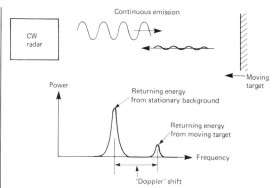

Frequency-domain analysis
If the CW radar considered previously now illuminates a moving object, radiation will be reflected back at a Doppler-shifted frequency. Some energy will return too at the fundamental frequency, from stationary objects. The frequency-domain analysis therefore reveals two spikes, and the Doppler shift will indicate target speed as

$$\text{Doppler shift} = \frac{2vf_0}{C}$$

where V is the target velocity (m/sec)
  f_0 is the radar frequency (Hz)
  C is the speed of light (m/sec)
  and Doppler shift is in Hertz

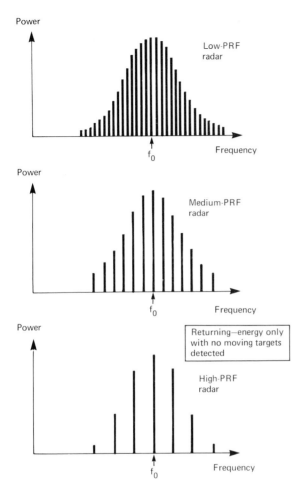

Typical PRF effects on frequency-domain analysis
A *pulsed* radar will detect reflected radiation at its
fundamental frequency, and see reflections too, although
slightly weaker, at regularly-spaced frequencies on either
side. The spacing is directly proportional to the radar PRF,
so they are widest for high-PRF radars. The relative effects
on a family of three radars are shown above, but in practice
the top two illustrations would be much more densely
packed, the upper drawing having up to a thousand lines
for each one on the lower diagram

analysed, and several examples follow. First is
the simplest possible radar; that is one which
emits a continuous signal at a fixed frequency. If
it is aimed at a stationary target all the returning
energy (which would normally be received by a
separate antenna, eg: radio altimeter) would be
at the same frequency as that radiated. The frequency-domain analysis would reveal a spike at
the frequency used by that particular radar.

With the same continuous-wave (CW) radar,
it is important to appreciate what happens if the
target is moving. Now radiation is compressed or
expanded as it is bounced off the object, so the
frequency of energy collected by the receiver is
slightly different from the fundamental fre-

quency. This is the Doppler-shift phenomena
which affects radio and sound waves similarly.
The sound from a horn, for instance, appears to
change from a high-pitch to a lower-pitch as it
passes on a moving car or ambulance. Such frequency shift in the radar energy reflected off a
moving target causes the spike to shift in the frequency-domain analysis, and the amount by
which the frequency is shifted is proportional to
the target speed or, more precisely, its range-rate.
This is the whole beauty of frequency-domain
analysis; that additional to the target range and
bearing data available from time-domain considerations, there is now the possibility of determining target range-rate from frequency-domain
considerations.

Incidentally, you can also think about deducing something about the target, based on the target frequency-spectrum. Propellors and turbine
blades can give recognizable patterns—but this
is a hint of research currently in progress and not
indicative of existing radar operation.

Unfortunately, because the transmitter blinds
the receiver, a simple continuous-wave radar of
the type described above does not lend itself to
a practical AEW application. When the transmitted signal is intermittent, as it has to be in a practical system, pulsing the radar energy compli-
cates the frequency-domain analysis task.
Whether the radar designer chooses to use either
the low, medium of high-PRF bracket has grave
implications, and his considerations are summar-
ized illustratively in three comparative plots
accompanying the text. These show the frequency-domain analysis results for different
PRFs, radiating into empty space. It is important
to note that returning energy is detected at regular frequencies spaced either side of the radars
fundamental frequency, the interval between
each so called 'harmonic' being equal to the radar
PRF. The quantity of radiation detected at each
'harmonic' frequency reduces either side of the
fundamental frequency.

In the discussion of PRF choices presented
earlier the clear advantage of low-PRF, in that
time-domain analysis was simple because no
range-ambiguities occurred, was made evident,
but a method of resolving medium-PRF range-
ambiguities, by using two or more similar PRFs,
was highlighted. This may not have seemed a
particularly sane complication to introduce at the
time, but now that frequency-domain requirements have been illustrated perhaps the great advantage of medium and high-PRF radars, in that
they have wider gaps between the fundamental
harmonics, and therefore are not as ambiguous

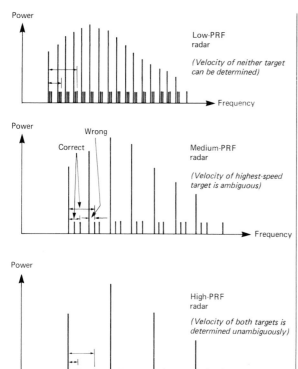

Velocity-ambiguities on low/medium PRF radars
Doppler-shifted spikes are received from each illuminated target. The frequency shift is unaffected by radar PRF so at low PRFs returning energy often cannot be correlated with the appropriate fundamental spike. At medium-PRF a high-speed target can often appear as a slow target relative to an adjacent fundamental spike. This is a velocity-ambiguity. On high-PRF sets there is sufficient spacing between fundamental spikes to determine the speed of all targets, unambiguously

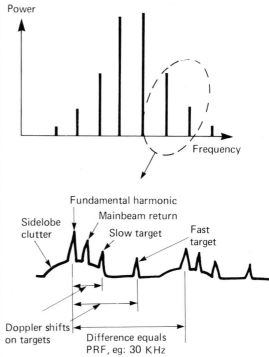

Detailed look at a frequency-domain spike
In real-life each spike on a frequency-domain plot is a complicated collection of frequencies. A wide lump is formed by sidelobe returns, and the better the antenna performance the narrower this will be. Embedded in each lump are two narrow spikes—one is on the fundamental frequency and the other sweeps either side of it, the position depending on the angle at which the main-beam is looking at the ground. Finally there are the target spikes, and at a certain velocity the slowest target spikes will merge with the moving main-beam spike. This imposes a limitation on the lowest-detectable target velocity

in target-velocity as low-PRF radars, should be apparent.

The illustrations of radar frequency-domain responses on page 36 have had extra spikes added, representing the responses which would be received from two targets. Note that the Doppler-shift is the same for both targets in each example, as the amount of shift is a function of relative speed and radar frequency only. In the high-PRF case the association of various target-velocity spikes to the relevant fundamental harmonic spike is quite clear. The medium-PRF responses are fairly unambiguous too, in the particular example shown, but at low-PRF the situation is totally confusing.

An additional consideration, which has not been hinted at so far, is illustrated in an additional set of diagrams, which show that although each fundamental harmonic has been referred to so far as a spike, in real life it is many frequencies forming a lump, in which is embedded the fundamental spike and at least one other

notable spike. These have to be expected in the real world, but there are some precautions which the designer can use to reduce the complications which they introduce.

The fundamental spike is partly due to transmitter leakages and reflections within the aircraft radome, but the second spike is a very unpredictable phenomenon. Its width is determined by such factors as scanning-angle limits, aircraft motion, electronic-component instabilities and dwell-time on target. Width is important as it affects the ability of low-PRF radars to operate at all, and the degree to which medium and high-PRF radars can see low-speed targets. There is nothing that the designer can do about these, except take such precautions as experience has shown to be necessary.

Most significant of all is the lump around each harmonic, which can threaten to fill in the gaps between adjacent harmonics. This makes a low-PRF radar totally unsuitable for target-velocity determination. The designer has some control over the width of each lump however, and can ensure that overlapping does not happen with medium or high-PRF sets. In the case of medium-PRF, where the harmonic spikes are quite close together, the width of each lump has to be as small as possible, and this is done by using an antenna which has very small sidelobes. Until the late-1960s these receiver-processor problems were very significant hurdles. Radar designers could see that the computing power they would need was likely to become available within the coming decade, but they had to work hard to reduce antenna sidelobes. It was in this period that slotted-waveguide and cassegrain antenna designs began to displace dish and Yagi antennas, and that the phrase 'pulse-Doppler' radar began to be used widely.

The value of target range-rate data

The preceding few sections have provided some explanation of the large increases in radar complexity, and naturally in cost too, through the introduction of medium or high-PRF capability and joint time-domain and frequency-domain processing. When the bonus is getting target range-rate data only it may not seem a worthwhile exercise. Surely, for instance, if a radar illuminates a target on every scan, say at five second intervals, and provides a measure of instantaneous position, would it not be possible, after a few scans, to deduce the target velocity? Simply put, the answer is yes, but the data, in general, would be unreliable. This is partly because the technique being advocated is arithmetic differentiation, which is always prone to giving a 'noisy' result. An example that would show this to anyone willing to try the experiment, is to read a car milometer at regular intervals, and to try deducing speed. The result will never be as accurate, or as instantaneous, as directly measuring the vehicle's actual velocity.

Instantaneous target range-rate data has a greater importance if the role of AEW aircraft is taken into account. Because these airborne snoopers are above most of the movements which their operators want them to see they have to look-down at targets (ships and aircraft in particular) against a background of land and sea returns. To the radar, that background appears to move, whereas it is the aircraft that is really moving. Because Doppler-shift only reveals motion normal to the radar's viewing angle, apparent ground or sea movements are not so straightforward as one might first expect. For instance, travelling at 400 kt and looking at returns from land, dead ahead, will reveal a Doppler-shift suggesting

that the ground is moving towards the aircraft at the same speed. Looking sideways at the ground will reveal no velocity relative to the radar viewing angle. Now, however, because the radar measures the relative velocity of every target (ground, sea, ships, aircraft, etc) it is possible to cancel those returns which coincide with what the radar computer predicts will be given by ground or sea reflections. In this way it can reveal aircraft flying at low-level or ships on the sea, whereas on a simpler radar these targets would be masked by 'clutter' from natural objects such as sea and land. Clearly a simple radar is inadequate for AEW operations, but a radar with the sophisticated kind of receiver described—the pulse-Doppler type—can manage the job. The designer has to tread carefully. In some applications the Doppler shift cannot always be trusted to indicate actual radial velocity. This is because modulations caused by turbines and propellors can give enormous apparent velocities.

The reason for having devoted a whole chapter to AEW radar technology is that, without all the capabilities described, the AEW role would not be viable. In subsequent chapters the relationship between AEW developments and the technical breakthroughs which have made all this capability possible will be charted, without resorting again to the detail covered in this chapter. It is hoped that the non-specialist will be able to refresh memory buds with a quick glance at the headings which sub-divide this chapter, and the captions and illustrations.

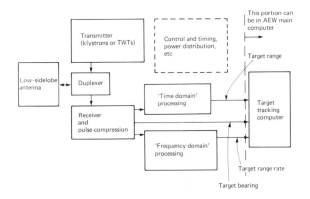

Elements of a modern AEW radar

A simple schematic representation of a radar was presented at the beginning of the chapter. Some detail can be added to that in view of the details discussed in the chapter, and produces a schematic similar to that shown above. *Antenna* is a low-sidelobe device, *transmitter* is either klystron or travelling-wave tube based, and *receiver* has time-domain and frequency-domain processors. The radar can include a target-tracking computer too. In an AEW aircraft this task is usually handled by the *main computer*, about which more is said in Chapter 5

A modern AEW aircraft results from an operational requirement, which the user writes before design begins. Modern requirements are so complex that only three AEW design teams exist in the Western world. AEW Nimrod, shown here, is the result of a Royal Air Force requirement written in 1974

Chapter 4
Operational Requirements

Airborne early-warning aircraft became necessary almost as soon as radar was put into service. The reasons why are evident in simple physics. Radar sets would not, and still cannot, see round corners (but that does not mean that they never will). Because radar waves travel in approximately straight lines, they cannot see into airspace hidden by the curvature of the earth, so the lower an aircraft flies, the closer it can get to a radar site before it is detectable. The facts are spelled out in an accompanying illustration, and the graph on page 40 shows that an aircraft flying at 18,000 ft (a typical bomber operating altitude at the time of radar's infancy) should be detectable some 170 nm from the radar. In other words, piston-engined heavy bombers of the type used in the early 1940s were visible almost an hour before they ever reached the outposts of a defender's territory. Even the high-speed high-altitude bombers which came along later were visible as much as a half-hour before they reached the radars.

When aircraft take cover, by flying lower, nature plays into the hands of the radar user. Halving the altitude at which an aircraft pen-etrates means a detection range reduction of barely 25 per cent. One message was clear, even before the final phases of the Second World War: to avoid radar detection, aircraft have to come in on the deck. A few figures will help to reveal the full story. A radar station located at sea level cannot detect an aircraft approaching at 500 ft altitude until it is within 28 nm, and if the target approaches at 200 ft it gets closer than 18 nm before its presence is evident.

Operations in this band of altitude were already used across the English Channel, by both sides, after the clear advantages offered by radar had become evident around 1942.

The targets more likely to face a low-level onslaught in those early days were coastal defences, including radar sites themselves. Over water the attackers could fly flat out without fear of hitting obstructions, and the only way that defenders could claw back some detection range was by raising the radar above sea level. When a radar is raised by 50 ft an extra 9 nm of detecting range is possible, and an aircraft approaching at 200 ft altitude will be detectable at up to 27 nm range. This figure is a theoretical maximum, and in general radar screens will be cluttered, so targets will appear only intermittently. With modern aircraft travelling 4 nm or more between successive radar scans it is inevitable that aircraft will get much closer than the theoretical maximum detection range before they are evident to an operator.

Inland targets are more difficult propositions to analyse. First, attacking aircraft tend to fly slightly higher, between 200 and 500 ft typically,

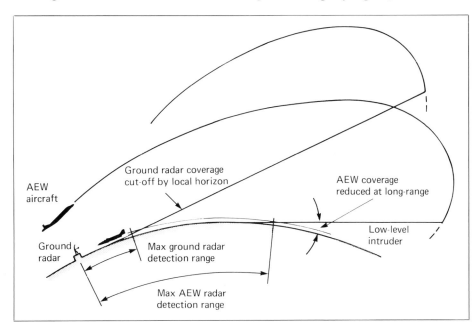

AEW aircraft

Ground radar coverage cut-off by local horizon

AEW coverage reduced at long-range

Ground radar

Max ground radar detection range

Low-level intruder

Max AEW radar detection range

This diagram, used by all AEW marketeers, shows vividly how an airborne radar can see a low-flying target at much greater range than a radar located on the ground and at the same geographic position to clear terrain and other obstructions, and a wily crew will also make use of terrain by flying in the shadow regions on the side furthest from the radar.

The defender's best plan has always been to locate radars as close as he dare to coastlines and borders, and at strategic points within his own borders. Even so, it has been painfully obvious, ever since plans to provide such methods of defence were first drawn up in the 1940s, that the number of radar stations required to protect an area of high-value targets means it is a costly business.

In the 1940s it was also time for sea commanders to question the vulnerability of their fleets at sea. If a radar mounted atop a 50 ft mast could not see an attacking aircraft until it was within 20 nm, ship defence wasn't going to be an easy proposition. The world's leading navies began to question whether they could have a ship and aircraft detection system much better than the visual maritime-reconnaissance aircraft types then in use. Both navies and air forces were drawing the obvious conclusion that the best way of seeing low-level attackers was to get radar sensors above it all. Airborne-early warning (AEW) was a buzz-word even before 1945.

The logic adopted was concerned solely with the threat posed by attacking aircraft, and this has become the central issue in all AEW operational requirements. Earlier in this book the presentation hinted at having a sensor which could watch all movements by an aggressor. However, how this ultimate form of enemy-movement detection will be achieved is still not clear. Radar has remained the primary sensor in all AEW aircraft for over 30 years now, and its main task has always been to detect aircraft (at all altitudes) and ships; and at as long a range as possible. Other capabilities have been incorporated if they have fallen naturally from the primary requirements, an example being the ability to obtain highly-accurate bearings on jammers which are beyond the line-of-sight of the equipment they disrupt on the ground.

The detection of low-flying aircraft and surface objects is the primary role of all AEW development, but several generations of radar development have been necessary to reach the full specification.

In the immediate post-war period airborne-radar sets were rudimentary. They usually operated at wavelength between 3 to 10 cm, and such short wavelength radiation could be directed quite adequately using a paraboloid dish, although high sidelobe losses were inevitable. At the time, only low-PRF sets were used, and when such radars were flown at high-altitude, around 18,000 ft, it soon became evident that if the radar beam was directed such that it did not reflect any

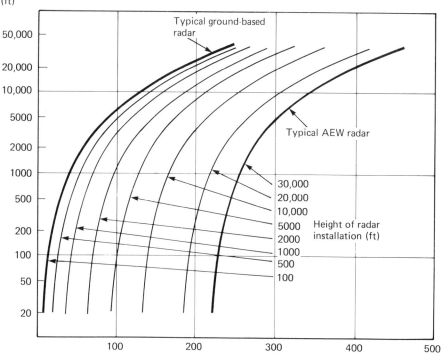

Plots of the maximum detection range for radar installations at various heights above the ground, and viewing targets which are at different altitudes, shows the clear advantage offered, especially in terms of low-flying target detection, by having an AEW radar at high altitude

This night-time radar picture of the Thames Estuary, taken from an aircraft around 1945, shows how even simple radar can reveal a lot of ground detail

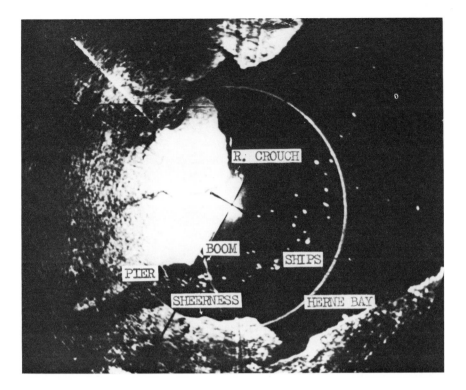

energy off the ground, it was able to detect aircraft at and above the same altitude, and possibly slightly below. In this guise systems were used in the first night-fighters. It must be pointed out that earlier aircraft which were called night-fighters had to be vectored by ground-based radars, even if they had simple airborne radars, and they were nowhere near as successful as future generations of autonomous night-fighter types.

Pointing the radar down produced a particularly important effect. Reflections from the earth's surface caused a big target to appear at a range equivalent to the cruising height, and unfortunately, due to the relatively large amount of energy being lost in antenna sidelobes, this would sometimes happen even when the beam was directed immediately ahead.

When radiation is reflected from land, it is reflected back randomly by grass, hedges, trees, buildings, and so on. Reflections from flat surfaces, such as water, tend to be directed away from the radar, however. On a conventional radar scope (called a plan position indicator, or PPI) the result of scanning downwards at close range is a map of the earth's surface showing strong returns from the land, and weak returns from water. Even a simple airborne radar can pinpoint a coastline, river courses and lakes. During hostilities in the Second World War this attribute was used to good effect, providing navigation fixes

from above cloud, or at night. As ancient considerations have located most cities and major industrial plants next to rivers, blind-attack target-fixing was possible too. Radars which can be used this way are categorized as 'ground-mapping' types, and it is a method of operation available on almost all airborne radars today, including the elementary weather-detection radars used in airliners and light aircraft.

Unfortunately, simple radars cannot detect details in the sense that one might expect. Those unwholesome sidelobes, and effects similar to the diffraction scatter which can be experienced with light waves, make small resolution virtually impossible. Radar is rather like an eye watching a scene through frosted glass, in that it can detect large-scale features, observe movement, and gain an overall impression of the scene which it is surveying, but the actual details of the scene is invisible. A consequence in the immediate post-war period was that overland AEW was out of the question; radars could produce a rough map, but objects such as low-flying aircraft could not be differentiated from the background. Low-flying aircraft detection was possible only over water, and under favourable conditions.

The building of enormously expensive chains of radar stations to defend land masses was accepted as inevitable. This produced several important defence systems. The Nato Air Defence Ground Environment (Nadge) is a chain of radar

stations along Western Europe's border with
Warsaw Pact countries, and the American Dew-
line stations are just one element of the immense
North American Air Defence (Norad) system set
up by the US and Canada. The British-deve-
loped UKadge (United Kingdom Air Defence
Ground Environment) is a much more capable
version of its first CH/CHL system. Some of the
capabilities of a ground-based air defence system
will be analyzed in more detail a little later, but
meanwhile attention can be devoted to overwater
airborne-radar operations, where almost all early
AEW operational experience was concentrated.

Over a flat area of sea an airborne-radar, with
a fairly large antenna (an important adjunct to
getting long-range target-detection) has a reasonable chance of seeing ships, and so it was in
the maritime-surveillance role that the first effective airborne-early warning (AEW) systems were
introduced. Radar-equipped aircraft, flown from
shore bases or off ships, and patrolling at high-
altitude, promised to provide long-range detection of shipping, and so forewarn the captains of
vessels operating nearby. Several aircraft types
were pressed into service in the radar maritime-

surveillance role in the late 1940s, and they were
categorized as AEW types.

In the decade and a half after the Second
World War AEW capability improvements were
very limited, due entirely to radar's poor performance when looking down at the earth. In the
late-1950s some military commanders, realising
that low-level aircraft were virtually invisible
even to AEW radar, regarded them as the most
persistent threat, and convinced industry to design aircraft specifically for such operations. It
is intriguing to look back now and to realise that
while the world's air forces still stuck to the development of long-range high-altitude strategic
bombers, ignoring all commonsense about radar-
detection capability and the missile-design
improvements taking place, it was navies that
started work on high-speed low-level attack
bombers. In the early 1960s a project sponsored
by the British Admiralty matured as the Blackburn Buccaneer and the US Navy wrote the
specification for the Grumman Intruder. Both
aircraft were designed to operate from aircraft
carriers, and their specifications called for them
to speed along, barely above wave crests, and

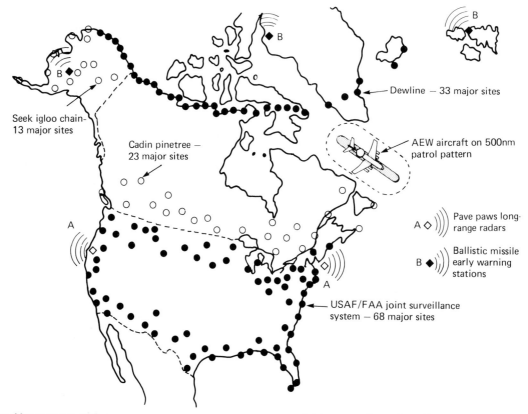

Norad long-range radars
The North American Air-Defence (Norad) network has a
very comprehensive ground-based radar system. Almost
100 radars, the larger missile-detecting installations being

spread right across the arctic and into Britain, are shown
here. Many hundreds of much smaller, short-range, radars
fill in gaps and protect the likely approaches to high-value
targets

attack targets at ranges of several hundreds of miles. As soon as these two significant bombers began to show their mettle they reinforced the need for an AEW sensor capable of detecting low-flying aircraft at long ranges. A lot of interims have to be reported first, but it is surely significant that it was in the same two companies that developed those first-generation low-level strike bombers, Blackburn at Brough in the UK, and Grumman at Bethpage in America, that the most enduring steps in AEW aircraft development were to take place in the ensuing decade.

AEW airframes were almost incidental. So long as aircraft were available which could carry the new types of radar-clutter rejection equipment becoming available in the 1950s they were pressed into service and became the first truly effective AEW types. Exactly what these new clutter rejection systems, called moving-target indicators (MTI) involved, is an intriguing tale of engineering ingenuity.

Early enthusiasm about radar operations from ground sites had been overly optimistic, the enthusiasm masking several fundamental drawbacks. One was to do with the effects of terrain, which would poke into the base of radar beams and clutter radar screens with permanent echoes. To nullify its influence radars had been installed on mountain tops, or any other prominent location. The result was that from radar stations all over the world, operators who worked in underground, cramped, and claustrophobic rooms, could at least enjoy panoramas that were worthy of best-selling postcards from their doorways.

But solitary mountains are rare. Geological origins more often than not dictate that when mountains well up from the plains and oceans of the world, they form formidable ranges and archipelogos. To the radar operator, those same mountains that made their place of work often enchantingly beautiful, made their job problematical. They would inevitably clutter the radar screens, so what was scenic to the eye was more than likely a nuisance to the radar.

When no high ground was available for a radar site, the result was disastrous, as antenna side-lobes produced reflections from the surrounding countryside out to 30 miles or beyond. To add a further injury, most early surveillance radars used 10 cm wavelength radiation, and these can detect weather almost as readily as aircraft. Consequently, on grey days, when even the view wasn't nice, the radar screens could be totally cluttered by permanent echoes from mountain sides and reflections from rain. This made air-

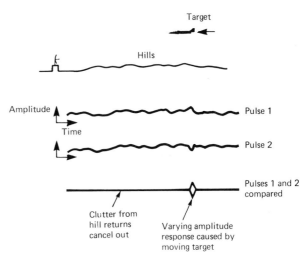

Coherent MTI
The amplitude of radiation returning to a radar from a clutter region, eg: over hills, will vary with time. By storing successive pulse returns and comparing the responses, moving targets are distinguishable by amplitude variations. This method of moving-target detection is used widely by ground-based radars. It is not useable in AEW radar however as ground-clutter amplitude varies continuously, due to the aircraft's motion

defence duties, and air-traffic control, the prime roles of ground-based radar, well nigh impossible.

Radar engineers reasoned that if the information returning from two successive radar pulses included returns relating to approximately the same clutter region, it would be of virtually identical amplitude at any given range. Anything moving however would produce a varying amplitude return. If the amplitude pattern from two successive scans could be compared, or even better, if several successive scan amplitude patterns could be compared, 'clutter' returns would remain the same, but moving targets would show amplitude variations. The concept is simple enough, and this is indeed the basis of most moving-target indicator (MTI) systems.

At the time of MTI's development, methods of storing electrical signals, even for the 1/500th of a second or so between pulses, were woefully inadequate. Remember that in 1/500th of a second, radiation in space will travel out 300 km, and back again. In a wire it would cover a barely less significant distance, but even a resounding signal sent down a 600 km length of wire will emerge hopelessly weak, and the physical task of getting such a long wire into an electronics cabinet defied comprehension. An analogous but more elegant solution had to be found. It came in the form of a 'delay line', in which the output is virtually identical to the input, but delayed by the interval between successive radar pulses. No

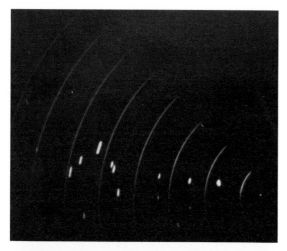

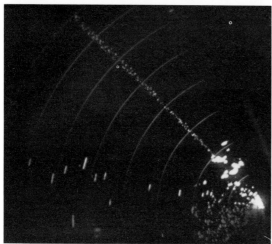

These photographs of a radar screen were taken a few seconds apart. The upper picture, taken when coherent-MTI was in use, shows aircraft clearly while the lower picture, taken when MTI was not selected, shows aircraft close to the station masked by clutter

energy is stored, but the equipment required to delay a signal by one PRF cycle is quite substantial, and a 'delay line' apparatus, as first produced in the early 1950s, was not the sort of thing to put in anything less than a furniture van.

To all practical intents the method was satisfactory. It is widely used in ground-based radars today, and called coherent-MTI. One drawback of its use is that if any moving target happens to cover a distance equivalent to an exact number of wavelengths between successive radar illuminations, the amplitude of the returning signal will remain constant, so the MTI system does not recognise its movement, and it is cancelled. This happens at regularly-spaced speeds, a typical coherent-MTI radar being blind to aircraft travelling at 80, 160, 240, 320 kt, etc. This is called blind-velocity fade, and although an

attacker might think he could bluff his way through by regulating his groundspeed to equal the known MTI blind-velocity, it is a virtually impossible task. An associated drawback of MTI is tangential-fade. In this case as a target moves abeam the radar, for a short period it does not move in the direction of expansion of the wavefront. Successive returns appear to have identical amplitude and are cancelled, causing the target to fade momentarily as it passes abeam the radar. Neither of these problems has been so severe as to prevent MTI being welcome wherever it has been installed. Operators get used to the system's idiosyncrasies, and between times, when the weather is good, they enjoy the view too.

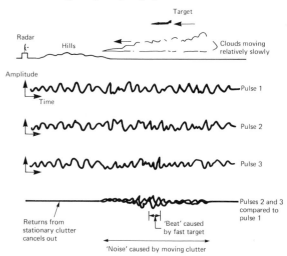

Non-coherent MTI
Coherent MTI cannot distinguish between slow-moving, large, targets—such as clouds—and an aircraft flying at high speed over or under the cloud. A more complex form of MTI was developed therefore, the basis of this non-coherent MTI technique being shown above. Several successive pulses are compared (usually many more than the three illustrated) and moving targets appear as 'noisy' portions. If the large moving object which is causing this noisiness has another object moving above or below it, the latter will cause a 'beat' frequency to be superimposed. This type of MTI is used in some AEW radars, where it is called airborne-MTI (AMTI)

Unfortunately, coherent-MTI is really too simple. A second form of MTI arrived, called non-coherent MTI. Instead of using amplitude variations exactly as received, non-coherent MTI compares amplitudes from successive sets of returning energy and determines 'beat' frequencies set up by fast and slow-moving targets, even if they are located at the same position relative to the radar. This will seem unnecessarily complex perhaps, but at least non-coherent MTI radar can identify blankets of moving weather, or areas of land, and aircraft above them. It cancels the weather returns, leaving on the screen targets which are moving relative to the earth and weather, ie: aircraft.

Non-coherent MTI has to memorize where it can expect to find beat frequencies, and when these conditions are not present it uses coherent-MTI techniques to determine clutter on its own. The requirement to memorise the conditions relevant to various areas of the radar coverage brought radar engineers into contact with data-storage techniques for the first time, and whereas digital computers with banks of data-storage are commonplace now they were very rarely used for on-line applications in the early 1950s. This memory-only electronics application, carried out using analogue equipment only initially, was a significant step ahead for radar engineers. The AEW radar fraternity watched non-coherent MTI developments in ground-radar installations rather jealously.

It has been stated already that when you put a radar set into an aircraft that is moving relative to the ground, it sees everything when it looks-down, the ground included, as a moving target! To add further to the AEW radar designer's dilemma, the world's oceans are continuously moving too, either driven by tides or pushed along by the wind. These effects cause waves to pile-up and reflect energy back when an airborne antenna looks along the direction of the wind or tides. The surface is textured, like land, *and* moving. Unless a non-coherent MTI radar is used there is no chance of seeing even a large ship, except at extremely long ranges when the vessel is virtually sil-

houetted, or at short ranges, dangerously close, where the sea texture can be differentiated from the ship.

Non-coherent MTI techniques therefore produced the first systems which got anywhere near meeting contemporary AEW requirements, and it is a great testimony to the skill of the engineers who made this important step forward, that the technical metamorphosis, from a furniture-van load of ground-based equipment to a carrier-borne aircraft load of black boxes, was made in the early 1960s. The system was called Airborne MTI, or just AMTI.

It was developed first in the US, and the US Navy had a special aircraft designed to carry the system; which crude as it was by modern standards has been refined over the years and is now the most numerous AEW system in the world. Further details of this, the Grumman E-2 Hawkeye family, are to be found in later chapters. Britain used earlier US-built long-range radars in its maritime AEW types, Shackleton and Gannet, but later added an indigenously developed AMTI, so non-coherent MTI technology was the lynch-pin of early AEW capability. The US and Britain were alone worldwide, such was the tremendous technical challenge involved in producing AEW equipment to these standards.

There was still a hole in the best defences. Even these sophisticated early AEW systems could not reliably detect low-flying aircraft, especially at long-range. By 1961 this was bad news. Aircraft such as the Buccaneer and

The Blackburn Buccaneer (NA.39) was designed to operate from carriers, and to attack at low-altitude, where radar could not detect it. This was the obvious way to exploit the deficiencies of ground-radar based defences in the early 1960s

The Grumman A-6 Intruder was the aircraft selected to fulfil low-level strike role from US Navy carriers

Intruder were already close to production, and projects such as TSR-2 and F-111 were in prospect. It was obvious that Soviet designers must be tackling similar projects, and that Western defences had to find an antidote. The quest for a radar technique able to give good 'look-down' capability, over either water or land, was being reinforced daily.

Operational studies conducted in the early 1960s showed that an AEW aircraft was needed which would cruise at 20,000 ft or higher, so that it could see low-flying targets across a wide front at 160 nm range or more. If targets had not been detected around this range, and defensive activities got underway before the target had penetrated a further 60 nm, there was a chance that too many aircraft would get through to the defender's ground targets, or even to the AEW aircraft themselves. In the intervening decades these figures have scarcely been reducable, the advent of stand-off air-to-ground and air-to-surface weapons having added at least a few more miles to the advantage of the attacker.

To all the electronic wizards in the late 1960s, one trend was unmistakeable, and it gave them reason to be hopeful of a new era in AEW radar development. Analogue electronics were going to give way to digits. The first integrated circuits, although almost trivial by today's standards, were about to enter production, and the promise of electronic reprogrammable logic in general-purpose computers was being viewed optimistically. At first, to engineers outside the inner clique of electronics experts, it seemed impossible to believe that the scale of what was being predicted would ever happen. Typical general-purpose digital computers in the early 60s had magnetic-core stores, which were relatively large and heavy, and the processing sections ambled through calculations at the rate of 10,000 or so additions or subtractions per second. Even a computer with a 4096-word memory still required a small office, a lot of air-conditioning, and suffered from mechanical and electronic headaches frequently enough to keep armies of technicians in business. They cost a lot of money too.

Within a little more than a decade the electronics engineers revealed the fruits of their optimism. They could provide as much as a million-words of storage with a processor able to add or subtract in less than a microsecond, and all this was in units barely bigger than a family suitcase. Equally as dramatic was a phenomenal improvement in failure rates, and a great fall in costs. The day of small general-purpose computers was suddenly a fact to live with, and with its arrival came the chance, if all other supporting requirements were met, to provide a radar with 'look-down' capability, in any weather, and over any terrain.

The pulse-Doppler radars, described in detail in the previous chapter, and nowadays almost standard items for high-performance military aircraft, were what eventually emerged. To some engineers this new breed of radars has been, or will be, a lifetime's preoccupation, and the capabilities being offered to the AEW commander are at last reasonably close to his long-standing operational requirements. Radars can now track low-flying aircraft, almost anywhere within their field-of-view, and irrespective of weather or terrain. Compared to what has been used before, these radars set remarkable standards.

It is clear already perhaps that the new-generation of long-range 'look-down' radars are bound to be mightily expensive to buy, and to operate. In leading aviation research establishments throughout the world numbers have been put into trade-off studies which have attempted to show how ground-based radar networks and AEW aircraft compare in terms of costs. Only Britain, the US, and if the aircraft which now fly are indicative of a bureaucratic decision of sorts, the Soviet Union, have decided that AEW aircraft are an investment well worth the cost of development and operation. Subsequently several other nations have decided that they cannot afford not to operate an AEW fleet, and have bought systems from abroad rather than face the cost of developing anything so complex.

Evaluating the relative costs of two aircraft detection systems which use different operating principles is an almost impossible task, but a simple example will illustrate the sort of analysis that is conducted.

A straight border, 500 nm long, is to be defended, and it is assumed that a radar located anywhere on the friendly side of the border can achieve the maximum possible detection range,

irrespective of any constraints imposed by terrain. Each ground radar installation is to be a site with the antenna 50 ft above the ground, and enemy aircraft approaching at 200 ft altitude are to be considered as visible 30 nm from the site. These assumptions mean that radar stations must be provided at not less than 60 nm intervals along the border, and consequently at least nine stations will be necessary to provide an unbroken line of radar coverage along 500 nm It is clearly impractical to place these radars right at the border, where they would be easy targets. At 20 nm from the border they would still be easy meat for tactical missiles launched by the enemy from his own side of the border, and at 30 nm they will be just a little more safe. With the latter arrangement, geometric considerations suggest that there is a 50 per cent probability of detecting attacking aircraft within 4 nm of the border, and of detecting all aircraft by 30 nm. In actual fact these are optimistic assessments, as it has been considered that any target detected at the maximum range credited to each radar installation will be immediately recognisable. Making a more realistic assessment will require too many subsidiary assumptions for inclusion here, and the clear consequence can only be that the number of radars installed must be increased. For the time being consider that nine installations close to the border will suffice.

It was quoted earlier that AEW assessments have suggested that attacking aircraft must be

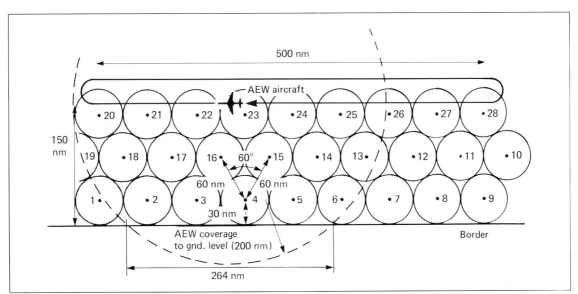

Ground-radar system and AEW patrol comparison
Above is a highly simplified example of how ground-radars and AEW aircraft can be used to protect a 500 nm long border. A ground-radar system of at least 28 radar stations is necessary, while a single AEW patroller flying at about

25,000 ft, 150 nm inside the border, provides equivalent cover. This example is covered more fully in the chapter. Later diagrams illustrate how to determine the number of AEW aircraft which are necessary

detected about 160 nm before they reach their targets if all conventional defence tactics are to be employed, so we have to assume now that all likely targets within the territory being defended are at least 160 nm from the border. To detect and track attacking aircraft over this distance requires three lines of radar installations, comprising 28 radar sites in total. The sort of coverage provided by this arrangement is shown diagramatically on page 47.

Those radars installed only 30 nm from the border certainly need to be defended, probably by a surface-to-air missile battery associated with each site. Indeed, it would not be unreasonable to assume that both forward lines of radar need to have defensive systems. It is not impertinent to note also that if all targets are at least 160 nm from the border then the intervening area is likely to be water, or at best an inhospitable tract of desert, swamp or other form of no-man's-land. The question of how one locates no fewer than 19 radar sites and their defences in such places, and revictuals and maintains them, deserves serious study.

If a nation has targets within 160 nm of its borders, and this is far from a rare occurence, it is clear that conventional ground-based radar systems will not be able to provide adequate warning of attacks for all precautions to be completed in adequate time. It would be impossible for instance to provide anything more than just a few minutes warning to a populated area, whereas about 15 minutes is desirable to permit residents to take cover.

The only alternative available with current technology is an AEW aircraft patrol. If a patrol pattern is set-up along the full 500 nm length of the border one aircraft will only be able to provide intermittent cover at any point, so the first priority is to discover how many aircraft are needed. First, assume an AEW patroller cruises around 30,000 ft altitude, and it can detect a target approaching at 200 ft altitude some 200 nm from its patrol line. If the AEW pattern is set-up 150 nm from the border, it will see approaching aircraft, at best, 50 nm inside enemy territory, and at any time it will provide full coverage along a 264 nm stretch of the border. If several AEW aircraft are used, and they all cruise at 300 kt in a clockwise pattern, it would be sensible to space them regularly so that each patroller's coverage sweeps behind the preceding aircraft. Ideally there would be sufficient aircraft for the coverage to remain uninterrupted along the border, in which case aircraft should fly at 264 nm intervals. This is regarded as unnecessary in real-life, as,

by having gaps between aircraft, considerable savings in equipment are possible without a great increase in vulnerability. In the example of a 500 nm pattern, if three aircraft are used, spaced regularly in the pattern, and cruising at 300 kt, gaps of around 15 minutes duration open between successive aircraft. Due to the racetrack type pattern aircraft in the rear of the pattern fill in between aircraft at the front of the pattern, and the diagram accompanying illustrates how gaps open only at the end of the pattern, and at two places along the border, each separated by 166 nm.

A bold enemy pilot might want to enter in one of these blind areas, during the 15 minutes that it existed, and if he entered as soon as the gap opened one might imagine that he could penetrate up to 150 nm. In fact, he cannot, as at all times AEW radar coverage is complete within 40 nm of the border, and now he stands being detected by not just one, but by two AEW patrollers. His task would be extremely difficult, his timing must be absolutely accurate, and the penalty of getting detected is that with two witnesses to the incursion there can be little hope of continuing to a target which is still over 100 nm distant.

This analysis shows that a three aircraft patrol, which would probably require a fleet of between 8 to 10 aircraft to be operated continuously, is a viable alternative to a 28 site ground-based radar system. It is easier to protect than the ground-radar system, and the detection performance is predictable with far greater confidence. But this does not mean that the cost comparison will come up with an absolutely clear answer.

Compared to a ground-based radar system, which can use many identical installations, each of modest technical capability, an AEW radar system is very expensive to develop. On the other hand, with fewer installations, even though each of them is a veritable airborne command-centre, the AEW alternative can be less expensive to operate. Most analyses show that radar stations will usually be competitive in terms of costs, over about 15 years, if the forward sites are not located in difficult terrain. Bear in mind however, that many other related costs which must be taken into account are ignored in the evaluation commented on here. For instance, it would be essential to provide a comprehensive method of coordinating activities throughout the total defence system, and the command and control systems necessary for each alternative might bear considerably different magnitudes of cost. Some discussion of the total facilities necessary for suc-

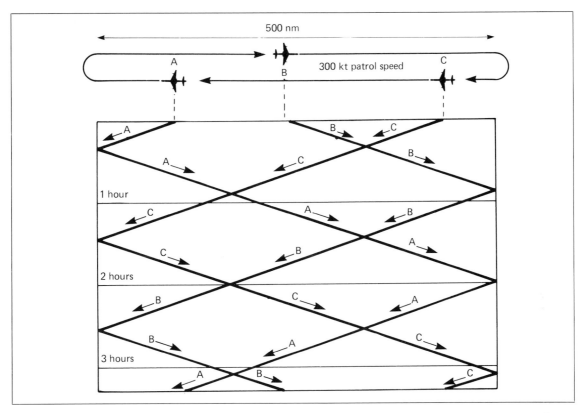

Using several AEW aircraft in one patrol pattern

Three AEW aircraft, regularly spaced in a 500 nm long patrol pattern, and each travelling at 300 knots, will complete one orbit each during a 3 hr 20 min period. To use each aircraft with equivalent effect they should be spaced regularly in the pattern

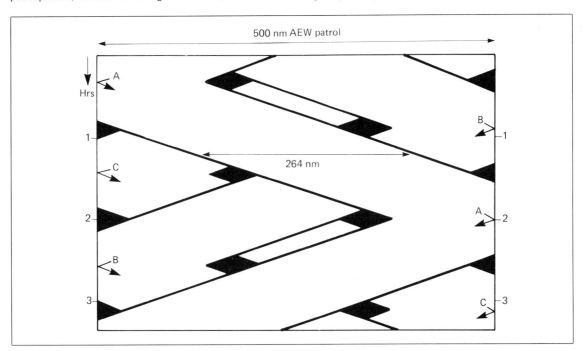

Predicting AEW coverage gaps

In the example illustrated previously, if each AEW aircraft could detect low-flying aircraft along 264 nm at the border, its protective capability could be visualised as a ribbon of the same width, as shown above, criss-crossing along the patrol pattern. The dark areas show where coverage gaps occur, and their total duration. These areas can be reduced or eliminated by varying the patrol-pattern length, AEW aircraft altitude, patrol speed or number of AEW aircraft

cessful AEW operation will be presented in the next chapter, and although the cost will appear to be considerable, ground-based radars do need a comprehensive support environment too. In a nut-shell, cost comparisons are not easy.

Reverting to a more realistic viewpoint, it was clear in the example above that assumptions associated with the AEW system were considerably fewer than with the ground-based radar system. In practical terms the conclusions from that experience are that if the border area is an ocean, possibly if it is inhospitable land terrain too, AEW has a great advantage, almost irrespective of the border length. This largely accounts for why the UK has always been a leading supporter of AEW technology. Alternatively if a border much larger than 500 nm has to be protected, the cost of a ground-based radar system can become extremely high, whereas a well-utilised AEW fleet will not cost proportionally more for each mile added to the patrol length. Again AEW can begin to show benefits, and it was from conclusions in this vein that the US, and possibly the Soviet Union too, found sufficient evidence to warrant the development of AEW fleets.

Small island states can almost always make a strong case for AEW protection, and so not surprisingly Japan has become an early customer for a non-indigenous AEW system. Nato, with its long border, and many high-value targets massed close to the line which divides East and West Europe, has been obliged to invest in an AEW fleet too, while a clear case of political necessity brought Israel into the ranks of AEW nations at a very early date. Countries such as Saudi Arabia, Egypt, Singapore and France are close to implementing AEW systems too. In general, as time passes, and as more long-range surface-to-surface and low-level strike penetration capability is brought to the hands of the leading armed forces of the world, the case for AEW protection gets increasingly stronger.

It would be wrong to give the impression that military planners are moving towards putting all their eggs in one basket however. All countries which have the technical ability to develop an AEW system can also implement effective ground-based air defence systems, and a combination of AEW and ground-based radars makes a sensible compromise. Established radar border-guard systems such as Nadge, the Norad Dew-line and Ukadge are all being strengthened at the same time as AEW operations are being introduced. Ground radars not only provide a fall-back element if AEW coverage falters, but they are more amenable to having sections hived-off to take on local control and defence requirements. Nowadays mobile radar sites are often used too. These can be relocated in a matter of hours, but to have this degree of flexibility does tend to increase costs, as more stations are required to ensure that full coverage is available while some units are on the move. A mobile radar system can recover from having a single element destroyed much more rapidly than a fixed-based system however.

The simple fact is that AEW capability does not come cheap. They are amongst the most expensive aircraft in the world to develop, manufacture and operate. When a nation sets its sights on developing an indigenous AEW capability it is embarking on a programme taking probably in excess of ten years from project definition to service entry, and in that period the programme will absorb the efforts of a team which will be in strong demand for uses elsewhere in securing the nation's defences. With the possible exception of France, which has a habit of doing things alone, sooner or later, and Israel, which has to face so many political whimsies that it too has a penchant for independence, there are no more nations who can be expected to find the will and the resources to join the leading league of three AEW producers. Yet the demand for these aircraft, even expensive as they are, can hardly be expected to diminish in the near future.

Chapter 5
Systems

Before embarking on a review of the AEW projects which have been implemented it is necessary to fill in some of the holes which have been left unattended in the descriptions so far. At a casual glance these may not be very evident, but by the end of this chapter the omissions which have occurred should have been put in perspective against all else on an AEW aircraft.

Over almost any area of the earth's surface, an airborne radar with 200 nm or more radius of detection will be able to determine the whereabouts of many targets. Over areas such as Western Europe and the US Eastern Seaboard up to 500 air-craft targets alone in daytime have been predicted. A typical AEW operation in such areas might suggest that a lot of seaborne targets would be illuminated too, and if all this was given to an operator to sort out, his task would be monumental. Systems have to be used to improve target identification performance, and then the information has to be got out of the aircraft. The systems described in this chapter are associated with these operations.

AEW patrol work undertaken in peacetime is as vital as wartime operations, even though the greatest proportion of the traffic detected at any time will be classified as 'friendly,' comprising commercial traffic plus military activity from the operator's own and associated forces. To identify aircraft and ships in these categories a system called Identification, Friend or Foe (IFF) has been in use, routinely, for almost thirty years now.

Two basic versions of IFF exist, one each for civilian and military operations. They are complementary systems, sufficiently similar to make

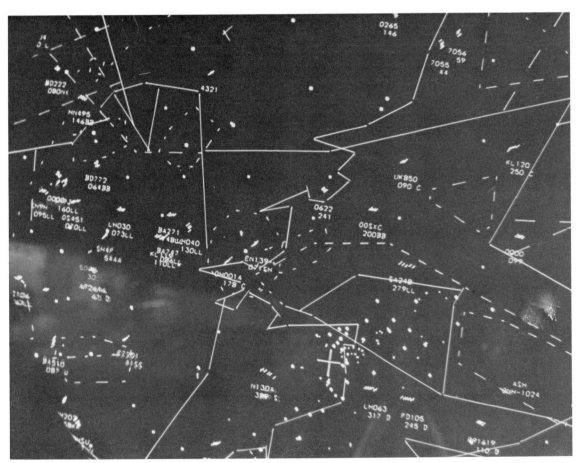

It is difficult to illustrate the enormous target-tracking task that faces an AEW radar operator. This photograph of airline traffic detected by secondary-surveillance radar equipment at London shows just how many aircraft can be airborne at any one time, and how confusing an AEW picture, which would cover a much larger area, could be

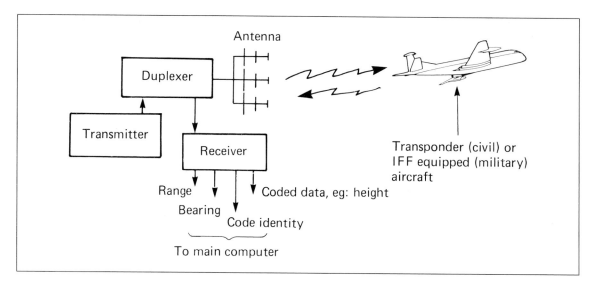

joint operations possible. The civil version of IFF, recognised internationally, is often referred to as secondary-surveillance radar (SSR). Similarities arise from the fact that all aircraft carry an equipment called a transponder. When this detects a set of pulses, arranged in a certain manner, it emits a series of pulses (the minimum number is twelve) which can be interpreted as a code.

Civilian aircraft have unique codes, the responsibility for code allocation being with civil air traffic control authorities. The authorities then use SSR antennas mounted on top of conventional radar antennas to emit sets of triggering pulses, which are called interrogations, and the responses are analyzed. The correct identity of each aircraft is assured, and the time delay between interrogation and response corresponds to the aircraft's range. Knowing the direction in which the interrogation was emitted, the SSR system provides sufficient information for the transponder-code position to be correlated with primary radar targets, and is a positive way of identifying aircraft. A similar system can also be used to identify ships in a busy port area.

If an AEW aircraft has a transmitter which emits the correct sequence of interrogation pulses it too can determine the range, bearing and identity of all transponder-equipped civil traffic within its area of coverage. Odd men out are the smallest general-aviation types, and these are usually obvious by their pedestrian tracks between towns and airfields. Apart from the occasional rogue, more than likely due to a transponder failure or a spot of finger trouble by a crew, SSR provides immediate positive identification of all relevant civilian air traffic and shipping.

IFF Schematic

Military and civil identification friend-or-foe (IFF) systems are similar. Although the civil system is less complex, and is often called secondary-surveillance radar (SSR), its operation is analogous to military IFF, and is illustrated here.

The system transmitter, either on the ground or in the air, emits many hundreds of pulses per second, at a frequency of 1030 MHz. A directional array of Yagi antennas is usually used. Any transponder-equipped aircraft which receives these pulses responds immediately with a set of pulses at 1090 MHz. Each responding aircraft pulse-set comprises up to 12 pulses, which when decoded reveal one of 4906 possible codes to identify the aircraft. Additionally, civil aircraft can add pulses which reveal aircraft altitude. Military IFF uses a much more complex coding system, and would not transmit altitude data in wartime operations

Directing attention now to military traffic, which incidentally can be identified by SSR in peacetime, the main objective is to differentiate between friends and foes, especially in times of tension. IFF is designed to do just that. The operation is exactly like SSR but instead of air traffic control allocating a code to each aircraft, the military co-ordinating centre for all battle activities allocates several codes to each aircraft, each one valid for certain time intervals. It is therefore easy to identify a friendly aircraft which is keeping to the ascribed coding procedure. Aircraft which do not respond at all, or which fail to make the correct code changes at the appropriate times, are classed as foes.

To carry out SSR/IFF interrogations from an aircraft an antenna, usually an array of small dipoles or Yagi aerials, is linked to the main radar. It is important to appreciate that although it might share much common equipment with the primary radar, IFF is a different sensor.

There is a temptation to regard IFF as a backup, but in its own right it is a very important source of operational information. For example, IFF on its own can detect all transponder-equipped aircraft and identify-each; it does not detect any aircraft without a transponder, or those operating with a failed transponder. On the other hand, radar on its own is able to detect everything of interest, but it leaves a big unscrambling job to identify and categorize everything. IFF and radar are each clearly complementary to each other, but they do not represent the complete answer by any means.

Having gleaned an indication of what is friendly, and what is not, it is valuable to be able to label the unfriendly traffic, identifying it in terms of being a bomber, strike type, fighter, destroyer, aircraft carrier, missile tracking radar, or whatever. Identification is sometimes achievable by listening to transmissions from the target. If it is a low-level bomber, for instance, energy from its terrain-following radar, reflected from the terrain around it, might be detectable. Certain combinations of emissions, either radar, radio communications or radio-navaid related, can be equated to unique types, or at least categories of aircraft and ships or missile installations.

To do this eaves-dropping an AEW aircraft

has to have a passive-detection system (PDS). This usually comprises sets of antennas arranged to give full 360°-coverage around the aircraft. Detected signals are fed to a system computer, perhaps several million pulses per second being received in busy periods. All the pulses are decoded and labelled, an extremely laborious task as the PDS will find all kinds of friendly signals mixed with the unfriendlies. To unravel the whole mystery calls for a very reliable library of typical sensor signatures to be stored and the sort of problems associated with modern systems signature identification will be highlighted later.

First, communication systems have to be explored in a little more detail. As described above the AEW aircraft role is achieved by a two or three-fold process, and this is an important point to make. AEW aircraft are not just radar pickets. They use a combination of radar, IFF and passive-detection systems whose aim must be to gather as much intelligence as possible on all activities in their area of surveillance.

Combining all this information, remembering that several hundred targets might be visible, plus that tracks can be established or lost at the rate of 25 or so per minute, and the enormous

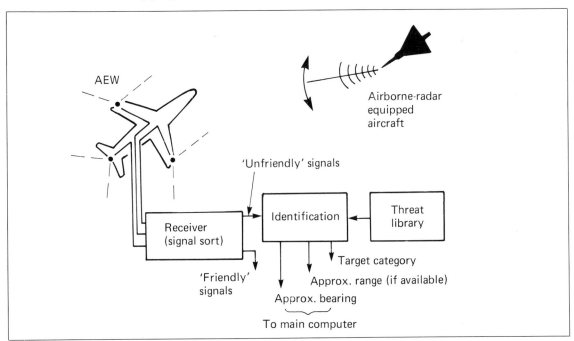

PDS Schematic

If any object emits electro-magnetic radiation it will be detected by sensitive passive-detection system (PDS) receivers on the AEW aircraft. (This system is called electronic support measure (ESM) on British aircraft). A very sophisticated, high-speed, receiver is employed. It may receive up to 2 million pulses per second and initially it sorts these into 'friendly' and 'unfriendly' categories. The friendly signals may be analysed in more detail, but the

other category is given highest priority. Target identification is possible in most instances by determining wavelength, pulselength and PRF characteristics and comparing them with data held in a threat library. PDS will usually reveal target bearing (coarse accuracy compared to radar) and may be able to determine the range of some targets. An indication of category: ship, fighter, bomber, etc is usually provided

degree of operational dexterity required is soon apparent. Because these are repetitive tasks, they represent the sort of chore that a digital computer can do splendidly. In most AEW aircraft, the tasks are trusted to a central computer, and they can be summarised something like this:

1 Storage of radar indications of the bearing, height range and range-rate of every target detected in its area of coverage. Revised information is added at regular intervals as the antenna is scanned.

2 Storage of IFF indications of the bearing, height, range and code of every friendly target which is equipped with a transponder. Revised information is added at regular intervals, usually at the same rate as radar data.

3 Storage of PDS indications of the bearings of electromagnetic emissions, possibly an indication of range, and where identification has been possible indication of its probable source.

4 Comparison of radar and IFF data, and where necessary PDS data too, to establish (over two or more scans) 'tracks' which correlate radar and IFF information.

5 Assigning an identity to each track, and asking an operator to acknowledge that there is a target of interest.

6 Maintaining a set of track files in which are held such information as target identity, height, speed and direction of flight. These files will be available for interrogation by operators at any time.

7 Providing data to operator's displays which permits labelled target information to be shown in the appropriate display format.

8 Providing access to information in store which is requested by any potential user through the aircraft communications system.

This is by no means a comprehensive list, and the experts at IBM, ESG, Marconi Avionics and elsewhere, who design such systems, could no doubt add a hundred and one extra items. The selection presented at least shows that vast amounts of data is collected, stored, sifted, correlated and distributed. It shows also that the central computer in an AEW aircraft is no trifling little machine, and as aircraft analyses follow some AEW central computers will be revealed as examples of the most complex software (computer program) design and development tasks undertaken in airborne computer applications.

In any AEW aircraft there are plenty more computers in addition to those already described. One processor will present navigation-system outputs to the crew, describing position so accurately that if the difference between computer and probable position was plotted on a standard aeronautical chart a micrometer would be needed to measure the distance. Another computer usually looks after radio navaid calculations, its activities in every microsecond representing

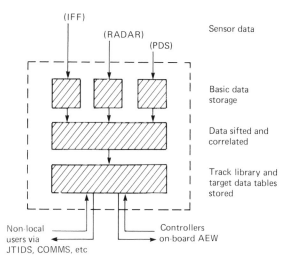

Main computer on an AEW aircraft
It is difficult to show how a large computer system works, but the flow of data in most AEW main computers is illustrated schematically above. Information is collected from a wide range of sensors and stored in its raw form, eg: range and bearing, and range-rate data. This information is then sifted and correlated, IFF and PDS data generally being compared with radar target data to assure accurate identification of the detected targets. Each target is then allocated a slot in the track library. This is what results from 'track-while-scan' capability, and up to 600 simultaneous targets can be stored in a large AEW system library. In the library targets are described by actual position, flight-vector (heading and speed) and identity tags. Anyone on-board the aircraft can interrogate the track library and the same data can also be sent by JTIDS or other communication links to other users

what has made many a navigator toil for minutes in the past.

Other little gems of electronic mysticism are hidden all over the airframe too, to monitor temperatures, fuel quantities, pressures and lots more. These are applications which arise on all aircraft types however, and they are not strictly elements in the AEW domain. Altogether, including these various little microprocessors, a system-packed AEW aircraft will carry more than a couple of hundred electronic computers.

One of the major uses has yet to be introduced; communication. It may seem remarkable at first that computers are necessary at all to look after communications, however, the capability which a military commander must have at his disposal if he is to conduct a co-ordinated campaign, and with the most up-to-date information, is daunting. The only way to present a description of communication systems which does not threaten to overrun the discussion of all other AEW topics is to develop a simple view of the problems which face the communications system designer, and to show how computers manage to provide an acceptable solution.

It must be appreciated first that an AEW aircraft cruising in its patrol pattern close to the stratosphere is a valuable sensor for many operations. The information which is stored in the central computer on-board will be useful to any battle commander's staff, wherever they might be on the ground, (or at sea) and to aircraft which are designated to defend the area of surveillance, or ships which are in waters scanned by the AEW's radar.

One way of making all the data in the central computer available to everyone is to code it and transmit everything on a high-speed radio link to the command headquarters, from where it will be distributed. This does mean however that the command headquarters is a communications bottleneck, and experience has shown that such a command structure is vulnerable to disruptions at the headquarters. Nowadays, major fighting forces insist on having at least two focal points which can conduct the command headquarters

role, so that the loss of any one will not be a fatal blow to the whole force.

Much less vulnerable is a fighting force where each fighting element, be it a small group of soldiers, a ship or an aircraft, can operate autonomously. If any element of such a force is destroyed there is, theoretically, no hole in the communications network. Although fighting strength may be depleted gradually during a battle, the ability for command headquarters to receive all data should remain unimpaired, and fighting efficiency should be little affected by losses.

In addition to requiring that the communications system should be co-ordinated across hundreds of fighting elements, and yet without an obvious controller (it is called a non-nodal system by communication engineers), there must also be little chance of messages being masked by enemy-introduced interference. Additionally, and again attempting to assure security, signals should have a low probability of interception, and even if they are intercepted and masked (the usual description for this activity is 'jamming'),

Boeing E-3 Sentry communications station shows the complexity of modern AEW radio-communications systems

the message should be difficult to mimic.

These requirements are long-standing, and even during the Second World War data-link systems were developed against broadly similar objectives. A data-link is radio communication using coded, usually intermittent, signals, instead of the modulated continuous transmissions used by conventional radio. If only one radio frequency is used the message code must be very elaborate, otherwise an enemy might intercept the signal and decipher vital information. An enemy who succeeds in that respect often will not jam the data-link channel. It is to his advantage if the user does not realise that he is being eavesdropped. Britain's success in breaking German high-command code during the Second World War was an example of such a strategy. A great deal of information was gleaned from the information being distributed by radio, and because jamming did not occur the German authorities had no reason to believe that they should take more care about the use of radio frequencies or the additional coding of high-security messages.

Nowadays, such a simple communications strategy is unacceptable. The only methods of radio communication which have been militarily acceptable for decades are those which use several radio frequencies. Switching between frequencies can occur either as infrequently or as rapidly as the user desires. It can be changed at random too. Messages are often split into small parcels which are compressed and transmitted as discrete chunks which the receiver has to re-assemble. Each parcel of information will often be

AEW aircraft are only the sensor portion of a well developed defence system. A Grumman E-2 Hawkeye formates with Grumman F-14 Tomcats—they will fly interception missions at the Hawkeye's command

sent using a different radio frequency, and if there is sufficient air-time available in the data-link system, all data is likely to be sent on two or more occasions so that even if one of the radio frequencies in use is jammed, then the full message will still be comprehensible.

The full horror of modern communication systems becomes apparent when one tries to envisage being party to such a complex message-exchange system. When can one start to transmit? What are the frequencies in use? At what instant will frequency changing be necessary? How long does one stay with each frequency? What is the code in use? The number of questions can be legion. This is all deliberate of course, as the more questions there are, and the more likely combinations of answers are possible, the less likely it is that anyone will snoop in on transmissions, and therefore eaves-drop, or jam, any vital information.

What does happen is that a very general pattern is established, and anyone friendly listening should be able to recognise it. The pattern can be defined as sets of frequencies, timings of frequency-hoppings, and so on. Anyone interrupting the pattern, at the appropriate time and with the appropriate code will be admitted to the overall communications system. Patterns are changed very frequently, for natural protection, and so too are the codes in use. We can be also sure that every military communication system has capabilities held in reserve for wartime use only.

It is worth recalling that a topic touched before communication systems was the eaves-dropping activity of AEW passive-detection systems (PDS). It is clearer now perhaps that a PDS has to be extremely versatile. Commercial radio and television broadcasts are examples of the extraneous data that might have to be filtered-out. There are also dozens of radio navigation aids, airliner's weather radars and ground surveillance radar stations. Usually (although nothing should be taken for granted in this game!) these categories can be ignored. After this, military radar emissions can be identified, more often than not with sufficient precision to recognize the type of equipment in use. Again friendly transmissions will be detected, and these should be ignored—assuming one is certain that the enemy isn't actually mimicking your own radio and radar. Finally, the location and operating procedures

adopted by aircraft, ships, ground-based defence networks and individual missile batteries is analyzed.

Knowing now that amongst this massive dose of data there will be a far from simple radio communications system too, how does a PDS unravel the enemy's radio communication system operations? If you want the full answer to that, and any other similar question, expect to spend a lot of time in a very secure occupation, and not to be able to talk about it afterwards. This really is the kernel of all modern military security, and no author like myself can expect to be briefed on modern communication or passive-detection system operations beyond a simple description of what will be evident to anyone who tries to eaves-drop a real-life communications system in operation. (And least that suggestion should encourage anyone to rig-up a wideband receiver and to get any impressions of reality, it is only fair to warn that in virtually every country in the world

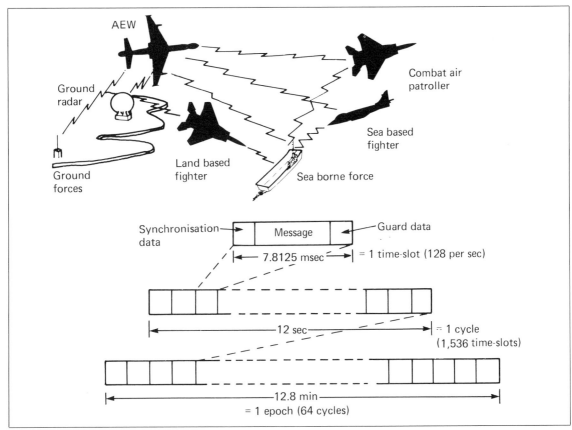

Joint Tactical Information Distribution System (JTIDS)

Provisions include:
* FREQUENCY-AGILE—virtually unjammable
* SECURITY-CODED—sophisticated cipher system
* VERSATILE—any user can talk to any other user
* HIGH CAPACITY—up to 98,000 simultaneous users
* RELATIVE NAVIGATION—Stations can broadcast position and any suitably equipped user can triangulate relative position
* WIDE AVAILABILITY—all major Western land, sea and air forces to be JTIDS-equipped
* HIGH-SPEED—large message capacity in each time-slot

such activities, even if they are inconclusive, are illegal).

Explanation of JTIDS (joint tactical information distribution system), formerly called TDMA (time division multiplexed access) by the US Air Force, is presented on page 57, with sufficient detail to extend a general understanding of communications systems features. It is being adopted by all Nato nations. In practical terms little else can be added, and readers who would find more detailed accounts fascinating would do well to ask how reliable is the content of some so called accurate articles which try to explain the numerical details of such systems. For any author to suggest that more can be said is irrelevant, as even a hint of the truth, revealed maliciously, or by chance, will almost certainly result in immediate changes to nullify the leak.

In that respect, something of importance can be said. To incorporate such versatility in a communication system, the users, whether big or small, have to be tuned in by very flexible computers. This does raise a very interesting point, because if a fully-operational communications system terminal is going to need an AEW-load of computing equipment, there is going to be lit-tle chance of getting everything into a small aircraft, or a soldier's radio pack. The dilemma is resolved by having categories of installations. An AEW aircraft, because it is a prime sensor, and therefore the source of vast quantities of data, has a high category, ranking alongside a command-headquarters location. It can originate or decode any type of message. A fighter radio, or a soldier's pack radio will be a lower category set, with limited capability. Such units, generally, will be the recipients of information, and they will absorb a lot less than an AEW can produce, but nevertheless the reasons for compact, microprocessor-controlled, radio sets are perhaps plainer to see now.

In terms of all the sensor and data-processing systems on-board, there is certainly more than meets the eye in an AEW aircraft, and the glimpse of the major uses of computers provided here should have highlighted how demanding AEW development can be. Sufficient in the way of scene-setting has been completed now for a review of AEW developments to be presented, followed by a look at the aircraft which have evolved to meet modern-day needs, and some of the problems of operating them.

Chapter 6
AEW Development

Many of the landmarks in AEW development have been mentioned already, but to see these in perspective against what could be done at the time it is instructive to run through the various projects which have ebbed and flowed on the tide of bureaucratic interest in AEW over the last few decades. The story alternates between America and Britain. The thread running through each of these two nation's development programmes is characterized by a steady flow of funding in the US, with occasional boosts when a major set of objectives have been identified, and a parsimonious dribbling of funds in the UK. The latter has been complemented with stop-gaps, periods of technical cannibalisation and, eventually, the foundation of the most ambitious airborne-early warning system development programme yet contemplated.

Britain's immediate concern, after it had begun to use ground-based radar to good effect in the early part of the Second World War, was the protection of strategic targets against the savage attacks which could be dealt by attackers who approached at low-level. The Luftwaffe had reasoned that as surprise attacks could be made against coastal targets, and as most of the radar stations which were blunting the effects of German bomber raids were on the coasts, these should be amongst the first targets to be attacked at low-level.

The radar stations were relatively lightly defended, and they had huge towers which held antennas 90 m (300 ft) or so above the ground—not really in an attempt to get low-level intruder detection, but because of those damned nuisance sidelobes again. Toppling such a large structure with the little bombs which the hit-and-run merchants could carry was not such a simple task however. Britain put anti-aircraft guns around its radar stations, and as low-altitude bomb dropping with the rudimentary aiming devices in use at the time was not a very easy task, all the stations survived. (One, at Ventnor on the Isle of Wight, was put out of action for a few days once, but that was the only casualty).

Stuka dive-bombers would have been effective at the targets, but they could not penetrate the radar defences, and Germany knew nothing about radar counter-measures until it was too late. The chances of Britain's radars getting off as lightly as they did were not the sort of odds to draw many gamblers, and there was enough said by allied commanders for Americans to take the hint that, isolated as they were, their coasts, and especially their fleets in the Pacific, were very vulnerable to low-level attackers. The consequences of aircraft carriers being destroyed regularly, or of a single Japanese or German aircraft hurling bombs on to a coastal city, was that the American public would soon believe that their lot was going to be the same as the battered cities of Europe. Project Cadillac, named after Mount Cadillac, Maine, where early trials were conducted, was initiated by Massachusetts Institute of Technology, and under US Navy funding, to reduce these possibilities.

Two aircraft were developed. Cadillac 1 led to an airborne radar being installed in a Grumman TBM-3W Avenger in 1943. Operable from an aircraft carrier, the AEW Avenger was the first of many Grumman contributions which appear in the story of succeeding decades. The Avenger used a high-power search radar; eventually it became the General Electric AN/APS-20, which

Junkers Ju 87 Stuka dive-bombers were ineffective against radar stations because of the height at which they had to approach and their low cruising speed

was used extensively. The system could detect shipping and, under favourable circumstances, low-flying aircraft. As already explained, a simple radar will detect ships relatively easily on calm water but as sea-states rise the chances of ship detection diminish. Aircraft detection is even more difficult. All this had to be learned, but the AEW Avenger was undoubtedly a psychological boost to US Navy carrier crews, and a deterent that Japanese commanders took seriously. In the Avenger there was barely sufficient room for the aircrew and the radar, so apart from a single radar operator there were no system's crewmen. All radar data was transmitted to the aircraft-carrier by data-link as raw video mixed with antenna pointing-angle data so that on-board ship a map of radar-detected shipping activity could be reconstructed.

By 1944 the US Navy had commissioned the first of several Boeing B-17G Flying Fortress as Combat Information Centre (CIC). These were developed as part of Project Cadillac II. They were the first land-based AEW aircraft, and were specifically tasked to detect Kamikaze aircraft. The B-17, redesignated PB-1W by the Navy, was

LEFT Once airborne, and with the undercarriage retracted, the Avenger's radar had an unobstructed view within the lower hemisphere. Lack of room on-board meant that only one operator was carried, radar data being radioed back to the aircraft-carrier

BELOW The world's first operational AEW aircraft was the Grumman Avenger. A result of Project Cadillac 1, it was deployed on US Navy carriers

large enough to accommodate the AN/APS-20 search radar in a ventral radome and a crew of radar operators, who were in radio contact with fighters which could be steered towards targets. Appropriately enough for a Boeing product, it was therefore also the world's first airborne warning and command system (Awacs) aircraft.

Very little information seems to have survived on the experience gained with the TBM-3W and PB-1W, but examples of the latter ended their days with the US Coast Guard, on weather-surveillance duties. Although they would have seemed reasonable enough in their time, neither aircraft is likely to have met all the claims which are often reported. Even so, in the forty years or so since, in the US, there has been a continuous

TOP Project Cadillac 2 resulted in land-based AEW operations beginning in 1944 using the Boeing PB-1W, a variant of the B-17 Flying Fortress. Like the Avenger, it carried a ventral-mounted AN/APS-20 radar, the only purpose-built AEW radar for almost two decades

ABOVE Underwing fuel-tanks on this Boeing PB-1W indicate its long-range capability. These aircraft patrolled off the US mainland, and eventually ended their days as weather reconnaissance aircraft

and undiminishing budget for AEW aircraft development and procurement. In that Project Cadillac sowed the seeds of what was clearly important to the security of the US Navy flotillas, and the nation, it was a very valuable exercise.

While Project Cadillac occupied America, the tables were turning in Europe. Britain was savaged less frequently, and by mid-1944 it was Germany who would have most preferred an AEW. In Germany, however, there was neither the basis for the development of such a system, nor the support. Germany had pioneered many offensive projects, but her ability to think so liberally about defence was tested too late to benefit the nation at all.

When the victory parades were over, most of Europe dismantled its war machinery as if it really believed that peace would be everlasting. There is no indication of any official effort to develop an indigenous AEW capability in Europe, beyond a stacatto embellishment of airborne-interception radar studies conducted by the Royal Radar Establishment (RRE), in Britain. Operational requirements which called for the long-range detection of relatively small targets, and against all manner of clutter, were apparently too ambitious to warrant any dedicated effort. The whole of Europe disregarded AEW requirements, with the sole exception of those few stalwarts of the RRE and the Royal Navy, who kept hoping against hope that some idea imported from the US might be sufficient excuse to prise money out of tight-fisted ministers. The latter however gave priority to huge jet-bombers which could cruise for thousands of miles in the stratosphere, and fighters and missiles which could knock the hell out of whatever similar bombers should ever be launched against them. All these new aircraft stuck out like sore thumbs on the radars which were now an integral part of all national air-defence networks, and the significance was largely ignored.

The same euphoria for superlative speed, altitude and range capability had gripped the US too, but there enough men who had suffered the hell of being onboard sitting-ducks in the Pacific were influential enough to keep ploughing a

LEFT US Navy specification for a torpedo-bomber in 1947 was revised as an anti-submarine type, and resulted in a pair of aircraft with different sensors, but which operate co-operatively. Both aircraft were called Grumman Guardian

TOP The AF-2W Guardian (sub-hunter) was equipped with an AN/APS-20 radar and carried two radar operators. In addition to its ASW role, it was also used as an AEW aircraft

ABOVE The AF-2S Guardian (sub-killer) had a small forward-looking search radar under the wing and carried armaments in the fuselage

steady flow of funds into AEW projects.

Grumman was set the task of designing a new torpedo-bomber. It was Project G70 internally, and XTB3F-1 to the US Navy, and unusual in having a single 2400 hp Pratt & Whitney R-2800-34W engine in the nose, and a little Westinghouse 19XB-2B jet in the tail. The latter was soon judged to be ineffective, and discarded, and at the same time the aircraft was re-assigned as an anti-submarine type. Two complementary versions of the airframe were developed. The first, XTB3F-1S, was a sub-hunter, and it car-

ried the by now ubiquitous AN/APS-20 search
radar in a ventral radome beneath the centre-section. Its stablemate, the NTB3F-2S, retained the
original internal weapon bay, and was little
changed by the re-designation, although it had
a searchlight in a pod under the port wing and
an AN/APS-31 short-range radar in an identical
pod under the starboard wing. Both machines
had side-by-side two-seat cockpits, and the
hunter version had two additional crewmen looking after radar operations, while just three men
in total were carried in the killer version.

The US Navy liked the performance of these
two aircraft, and they were re-designated as AF-
2W and AF-2S for hunter and killer versions respectively. Grumman had re-assigned them as
Project G82, and in service they became known
as the Guardian. The first examples entered service in late-1950, and deliveries ended in March
1953, after 153 AF-2W and 193 AF-2S airframes
had been produced. No stretch of the imagination
would bring anyone to regard an anti-submarine
type as an AEW aircraft today, but in their day
they were real pioneers in the art of searching out
submarines at long-range plus, if conditions were
good, the radar could detect low-flying aircraft
at relatively short-range. The Grumman Guar-

dian, based on this interpretation, is popularly
regarded as the world's first AEW aircraft.

Slightly later in timescale, the Douglas AD-
3W Skyraider was also fitted with a General Electric AN/APS-20 radar in a radome similar to that
used on the Guardian hunter. It also carried two
radar operators, but this time with only one pilot.
Radar performance was still rudimentary, detection capability being affected greatly by sea-state
and, to a lesser extent, by meteorological phenomena, but the faltering steps towards comprehensive AEW were being taken.

By 1952 AN/APS-20 was already regarded as
the doyen of all AEW radars. It had been
designed to US Navy requirements in the late-
1940s by Hazeltine Corporation, but the production contract was awarded later to General Electric. Operating frequency was in S-Band (2 to
4 GHz frequency) and developed versions of the
radar, used in later versions of the Skyraider,
could detect medium-sized aircraft at about
50 nm range. A 1.8 m (6 ft) wide dish antenna
and a cavity magnetron transmitter were used.

A frustration which plagued early users of the
AN/APS-20 was its unreliability, which in the
main was attributable to the magnetron. First, it
was operated at a very high rating, which did not

Mainstay of US Navy fleet AEW operations throughout the fifties was the Douglas AD-3/4 Skyraider, of which 417
examples were built

Two Lockheed PO-1W aircraft, based on the Constellation airliner, were evaluated with combined search and height-finding radars during 1949–1950

BELOW Production Lockheed WV-2 AEW aircraft for the US Navy were based on the Super Constellation and entered service in the early fifties

help, but additionally it was adapted from a ground-based radar and had a cantilevered cathode which was easily displaced by the jolt of a hard carrier landing. The latter fault was not always apparent until the radar was operated at full power, which was never possible on a carrier, so Skyraider operators tended to get used to having a radar failure reported soon after take-off. It was a small problem, but one with an immense operational implication, and yet because it was difficult to rectify without affecting the fundamental operation of the radar it took many years to incorporate suitable modifications.

The Skyraider was produced in sizeable numbers, nevertheless. Production for the US Navy totalled 417 aircraft, 31 designated AD-3W, 168 examples of the AD-4W (including 50 aircraft supplied to the Royal Navy) and 218 AD-5Ws. The latter were redesignated EA-1E in 1962.

Following on from its experience with the Boeing PB-1W, in June 1948 the US Navy placed a contract with Lockheed for a further land-based AEW aircraft, this time based on the Constellation airliner. The PO-1W variant of this beautiful aircraft, later re-designated WV-1, was a grotesque sight in its time. The first of two prototypes, both based on the short-bodied Model

749, flew at the hands of Joe Towle, Roy Wimmer and Carles Mercer on June 9, 1949. Although handling was reported to be good Towle experienced some 'directional stubborness', and to remedy this a 45 cm (18 in) vertical extension was incorporated in each outer fin. This modification was later made standard on the Super Constellation and all its derivatives. The second WV-1 flew in December 1950 and was the last military Constellation to be built.

A profusion of aerials, 39 in total, was dominated on each aircraft by a 2.13 m (7 ft) high radome on top of the fuselage, and a shallower, but much wider, radome under the fuselage. Within the airliner several tons of electronics was crammed into the cabin and under floor holds. The search radar in the ventral radome was again the General Electric AN/APS-20, and in the dorsal radome there was a height-finding radar, which when turned to face any selected target would scan vertically to determine the target elevation.

The two WV-1s were delivered to Naval Air Station Patuxent River, Maryland, and completed evaluations which included Nato manoeuvres during 1951 and 1952. At the time of 'Operation Mariner' in 1951 they were the only US Navy aircraft able to fly because of heavy seas

and foul weather, but by all accounts they acquitted themselves well against land-based types that flew out to sea and tried to return as raiders. It was a performance that set the production line alive at Lockheed.

When ordered into production the longer fuselage of the Model 1049 Super Constellation was selected, and the aircraft joined the US Navy fleet as WV-2. Five operator's positions were provided and intercommunication include a television system which allowed each controller to read data written on a central camera-monitored display board. The CIC (Combat Information Centre) concept adopted in the Boeing PB-1W was extended too, so that the airborne command post could talk directly to ships, shore-bases and aircraft. Up to 32 crewmen were carried on long sorties.

The WV-2 so impressed the USAF that it ordered the aircraft in 1951, and made it a familiar sight in many parts of the world. The aircraft was re-designated EC-121C, and was officially named Warning Star. Production of all radar-equipped, and related electronic-countermeasure versions of the same airframe, totalled 142 aircraft, and on Lockheed accounts that amounted to $125 million-worth of business.

The basic EC-121C carried 6550 US gallons of fuel, and had a maximum endurance of 18 hours. A later version was the EC-121D which had two 600 US gallon tip tanks and an additional 1000 US gallon belly fuselage tank, extending maximum endurance to around 25 hours. The last USAF EC-121 operation was from Keflavik, Iceland, in 1976, and a few aircraft were active with the US Air Force Reserve until eventual re-

tirement in October 1978.

While all this was going on in the US, the lessons of AEW had been forgotten by the Treasury in Britain. Instead of encouraging UK industry to build its own AEW system, the response to strong lobbying from the Royal Navy was to authorise procurement of 50 examples of the Douglas AD-4W Skyraider. Each British carrier now had its own AEW, and as far as the ministers of the day were concerned it was excellent because it couldn't have been done cheaper.

Britain was more concerned than most nations with anti-submarine warfare, and did make a notable start in the field by flying the first Avro Shackleton GR.1 in March, 1949. An improved version, the Shackleton MR.2 flew on 17 June 1952, with a search radar in a ventral radome. This was recognized as an ideal platform for future AEW work and many years later it was equipped—as you might have guessed—with US-built AN/APS-20 radar in a ventral radome attached directly beneath the cockpit, thus

TOP US Air Force land-based AEW operations began in 1953 when WV-2s, designated EC-121 (and later re-named RC-121 Warning Star), were introduced. This EC-121H operated by the 551st AWAC Wing was photographed at Kevlavik, Iceland. Examples of this type remained in service until 1978

BELOW LEFT Royal Navy fleet-protection requirements were met by the Douglas AEW.1 Skyraider (a variant of the US Navy AD-4). About 50 examples operated from British aircraft-carriers throughout the fifties

BELOW Land-based AEW operations began in Britain in 1972 when the Royal Air Force took delivery of its first Avro Shackleton AEW.2. Continually revamped, the Shackleton was still the RAF's leading AEW type in 1983

becoming the Shackleton AEW.2. These far from sophisticated airframes were to soldier on for over thirty years, becoming the longest-serving air-frame used in an AEW role. A major re-organization of Shackleton operations took place in 1972, of which more is said when the reasons why have been developed later in this chapter.

Britain had considered the licence production of AN/APS-20 sets, and proposals were submitted by Elliott Brothers around 1955 to manufacture some 80 installations. Subsequently the Gannet production programme was cut back, leaving a requirement for about three dozen sets only, a number which was too low to warrant investment and tooling for the job. Elliots therefore took on the UK support contract for the radar. The company manufactured and supplied spares during the years of RAF/RN operations with the sets, and also gained an insight into AEW radar problems by working alongside service personnel conducting fault isolation and modification programmes. It was experience that

would prove none too little when Britain eventually bit the AEW bullet in the 1970s.

Meanwhile, the massive girdles of radar stations which have become the backbone of Norad and other air-defence networks were being assembled. Some of these radar stations, perched on isolated mountains, or buried in snow and ice on Arctic plateaux, have to be seen to appreciate how much they can cost to build and operate.

Within these radar stations the saga recounted in the chapter on operational requirements was coming into play around the mid-1950s, with the first operational use in ground radars of coherent moving-target indicator (MTI) systems. The end result of this equipment—the banishment of virtually all permanent echoes on the radar screen—was a step forward which made ground-based radar immediately as effective as radar proponents had been claiming, all along, that they always had been. Even today, the man in the street very rarely appreciates just how diaboli-

The massive proportions of the WF-2 radome, in relation to the airframe, and the way that the original aircraft fin was cut away, are features evident in this view

The Grumman WF-2 Tracer was the first AEW type to use a radar antenna enclosed in a dorsal radome. It was designed to a US Navy specification which set the trend for future AEW operational requirements

cally poor a simple radar is when it is used as a ground-based surveillance aid. Without the capability provided by coherent-MTI few radars come anywhere near meeting their target-detection requirements.

Following close on the heels of coherent-MTI was non-coherent MTI. This second step forward overcame one disadvantage of its predecessor. Because it could determine the relative movement of two objects illuminated at the same place, it was able to differentiate between slow-moving and fast-moving objects. Air-defence radar specifications had sought this capability because with coherent-MTI an aircraft flying over a clutter region which was moving (a large cloud could be sufficient) could not be differentiated from the clutter. The capability was what an AEW aircraft radar wanted: a means of looking down on to objects flying over the Earth, which moved relative to the radar because of the aircraft's motion.

One might ask why AEW research hadn't spawned non-coherent MTI, and there can never be an adequate answer. However, being practically-minded people, the AEW researchers had set their hearts on finding a solution that would fit into an aircraft. The ground-surveillance radar non-coherent MTI system of the mid-50s might be transportable in a Boeing 747 today, but it was incomprehensibly big for the aircraft of its day. Nevertheless, General Electric was awarded a US Navy contract to consider the miniaturization of non-coherent MTI in the mid-1950s. It was an event that happened unannounced, but it was to revolutionize AEW history.

At the same time Grumman was rolling out the prototype of a new AEW aircraft for the US Navy. It was a squat adaptation of the anti-submarine S-2F Tracker. The new aircraft, designated WF-2 Tracer, flew on March 1, 1957, had an aerodynamically-shaped glassfibre honeycomb radome fixed above the fuselage. It contained a Hazeltine AN/APS-82 radar with a 4.27 m (14 ft) wide scanner. Compared to previous types the radar was massive, and modifications to the aircraft to accommodate the new radome included lopping off the large fin used on the Tracker, and replacing it with twin fins. The stub of the truncated original fin was used as an attachment on the back of the radome. Much of the detail on the AN/APS-82 owned a lot to the faithful AN/APS-20. The much larger scanner, and a series of transmitter modifications which reduced its peak power output, contributed to better long-range detection performance and improved reliability. The effective range against

a typical target was increased about two-fold, so that under favourable conditions an aircraft was now detectable at 80 to 90 nm range.

Meanwhile, by 1957 General Electric's engineers were telling the US Navy that the long-shot contract placed earlier was not quite the long-shot that many had anticipated. They could see ways of introducing pulse-compression techniques and non-coherent MTI, from then on called airborne MTI (AMTI) by the AEW fraternity, into radars that would fit into an aircraft. In fact, everything was looking so good that given another year they might get the radar volume down from a Super Constellation load to something that would fit into an aircraft considerably smaller.

A lot more was happening too, and before the thread that ran on from this significant programme is picked up again, a brief look at the state-of-the art, and of what other innovations were around is necessary.

Installationally, two major concepts had been established, based on either ventral-mounted (below the fuselage) or dorsal-mounted (above the fuselage) antennas. Ventral radomes had been very popular, but they are restricted in depth by ground-clearance requirements. Undercarriage geometry also usually restricted the radome width, and on carrier-borne types this was a distinct disadvantage. On the credit side for the same installation is the fact that, if the aircraft's undercarriage retracts, the radar has an unimpeded field-of-view around and below. Dorsal-mounted radomes have fewer restraints on dimensions, but suffer blanking due to the airframe at short-ranges, yet at about this time a second factor was beginning to emerge as particularly important to the installation arguments: longer wavelength operation was being received more favourably. (In due course a move back to the waveband used by the AN/APS-20 was made, but more about that later). Radiating longer wavelengths required a larger radar antenna, however, and the Tracer configuration offered an insight into the kind of dorsal installation that might have to be faced.

The US Navy remained firmly convinced of the need to use land-based AEW aircraft too, and an experimental version of the WV-2, the WV-2E, flew briefly with a saucer-shaped rotodome—the first symmetrical rotating dorsal installation—which was no less than 11.3 m (37 ft) in diameter. It would appear that this inspired Soviet designers a lot, the configuration being faithfully reproduced on the Tupolev Tu-126 Moss which first flew almost a decade later. The

The world's first rotodome—a radome which is rotated with the antenna it encloses—was flown on the sole Lockheed WV-2E in 1956. This type was never put into production, but the rotodome has been used on all US AEW types since. The WV-2E installation was also faithfully copied on the Soviet Tu-126 Moss

WV-2E did not progress any further in the US, although the rotodome concept was to be given approval.

Britain was meanwhile preparing to replace the Douglas Skyraider AEW.1s which had been purchased from the US with an indigenous product, the Fairey Gannet AEW.3, which was designed again to accommodate the AN/APS-20 radar in a relatively small ventral radome. The Gannet AEW.3 first flew on August 20, 1958, and capable and trustworthy as it was in service over the next two decades it is sad to relate that beyond two radar improvement programmes, nothing was done to further improve AEW cover available to British fleet operations at sea.

The first of the British improvement programmes was in the mid-1960s after a joint survey conducted by Royal Navy and Elliott engineers had recommended the installation of IFF interrogation capability, a video accumulator (a device which retains only what is overwritten on display sweeps and can therefore reduce the effects of random-noise jammers) plus a parametric amplifier, on all UK AN/APS-20 systems. These modifications were acceptable to the Admiralty and were introduced, but a scheme to replace the small 13 cm (5 in) diameter operator's displays with a larger unit were ruled out due to installation constraints. The latter modification would

A Gannet AEW.3 showing its ventral radome. The aft section of the radome was scalloped to provide wheel clearance during the undercarriage retraction sequence

TOP RIGHT British fleet operations began with an indigenous aircraft in 1961 when the Fairey Gannet AEW.3 entered service. Much bigger than photographs tend to indicate, the Gannet was essentially twin-engined with two Mamba powerplants geared to drive contra-rotating propellors

RIGHT A Royal Navy Gannet AEW.3 takes off from the angled deck of a British carrier, without catapult assistance

have also introduced a moving cursor facility.

Radars installed in the Gannet AEW.3 comprised a 2.3 × 0.9 m (7.5 × 3 ft) antenna in a ventral radome which was pear-shaped with the fattest portion forward. Scalloping in the aft region provided clearance for undercarriage retraction. There was a three-man crew; pilot and two radar operators, and maximum detection range of large targets was about 100 nm.

Royal Navy testing was conducted by No. 700G Intensive Flight Trials Flight, and in the course of 17 months, to January 31, 1960, only three aircraft were used to complete a 1,855 hour evaluation programme. Initial deck landing trials took place on HMS *Centaur* in November 1958, and in February 1960 700G Squadron was reformed as Fleet Air Arm 849 Squadron, and commenced operations on HMS *Ark Royal*. About 30 Gannet AEW.3s were delivered by 1962 when production ceased. All received an AMTI receiver system in an update programme during 1972–1973, and HMS *Ark Royal* retained

the Gannet AEW.3 complement until it was taken out of service in 1978. Following this there was no shipborne AEW for Royal Navy when at sea, until the cataclysmic lessons of the Falkland Islands Campaign in 1982.

American industry had cottoned on to the idea of using airships, an idea that was especially attractive since the low speed of these vehicles suggested that they should not need anything more than a simple coherent-MTI system. Goodyear developed the ZPS-2W, a non-rigid helium-filled envelope of 27,590 m³ (975,000 ft³) capacity. It has a height-finding radar perched on top of the envelope, supported by a 75ft-high rubberized fabric tunnel, and the search radar was in a swollen appendage beneath the airship gondola. An antenna measuring 5.3 × 1.2 m (17.5 × 4 ft) was used by the search radar (another AN/APS-20) and an endurance of 58 hr was claimed. Endurance records in excess of 200 hrs were set, but clearly crews are not able to maintain their efficiency when asked to perform their

The Goodyear ZPS-2W airship had its main antennae mounted on top of the hull. This was an experimental configuration which looked very promising in the late-fifties

RIGHT Had AEW airships gone into production, the favoured design was the Goodyear ZPG-3W, which displaced 1,500,000 ft³. AEW airship development was overtaken by the US Navy-sponsored AMTI-radar development programme

duties for 8 days non-stop in such a cramped workplace.

The ZFG-2W trials were so promising that an even larger airship was built. The ZFG-3W used a 42,500 m³ (1,500,000 ft³) envelope, and it had a 12.8 × 1.8 m (42 × 6 ft) antenna UHF-wavelength inside the gas enclosure. I have often wondered since whether gas swirling around such a large antenna inside the confines of the enclosure would have had any noticeable effect on the airship's manouevrability. Someone, somewhere is bound to know, but the answer to such thoughts can only come from memories for the airship experiments were soon overtaken.

At about the same time, diligent stalwarts in Britain had succeeded in getting funds, at last, to conduct AEW radar experiments with tethered balloons. The tests were conducted by RRE personnel around 1958 and, as far as can be discovered, no one has dared to admit publicly that the experiments took place. Perhaps it was feared that someone would claim that money was being squandered on a fanciful project. While airship interest waned quite rapidly shortly afterwards, the fact that someone in Britain was able to see that airship AEW was a practical proposition is faintly heartening. What a pity that the British public was not told earlier.

Finally, Britain had got one other decision absolutely right. On April 30, 1958 the prototype Blackburn NA.39 made its maiden flight. Later to become the Buccaneer and to be perhaps the most successful low-level strike bomber of its era, the Buccaneer would be an intolerable menace to anyone who hadn't got AEW defences. It was designed to sneak in at below 200 ft altitude, at speeds in excess of 500 kt, and in those days nothing could touch it. One other aircraft was being assembled in the US which would operate similarly, and that is the only reason why the Buccaneer cannot be proclaimed outright as the best low-level strike type of its era. The Grumman A-6 Intruder was designed to an almost identical specification. During the remainder of this chapter, as progress in the 1960s is traced, it will be intriguing to see how often the pioneers in low-level strike aircraft design, the Blackburn team at Brough—under Hawker Siddeley auspices after 1962—and the Grumman team at Bethpage, kept very close to current AEW technology.

Now, however, it is time to look at what General Electric reported to the US Navy in 1958. The company had discovered that, given time and money, a UHF-wavelength radar could be combined with an AMTI processor, and made to weigh about three tons. The latter figure happened to be the sort of target that US Navy officials had reasoned could be installed in a carrier-borne aircraft. The great stride that this represented, at the time, is difficult to put across. To the AEW fraternity it seemed like jumping out of biplanes into swept-wing jets, in one generation.

The US Navy turned to its most experienced AEW contractor, Grumman, and told the designers at Bethpage to co-ordinate with the radar gurus at General Electric. If there was any chance of getting a 360°-surveillance AEW system, operating at UHF-wavelengths, and with an AMTI processor included, into a carrier-sized aircraft, the consequences for fleet protection were unprecedented. By 1959 the dream was looking good. In the same year contracts were put on Grumman and General Electric to commence development of what was to become the E-2 Hawkeye airframe and the AN/APS-96 radar. In an aircraft only a little larger than the WF-2 Tracer—which was only just entering service—there was to be a capability that not even the mighty Constellation could match. At a stroke the Goodyear airships were made redundant. It looked as if everything was going to give way to this dramatic breakthrough.

There was an element of risk involved however, and the Tracer programme soldiered on for a few years. The E-2A which used the new radar was not deployed for another six years, and it was a few more years before AMTI came along. The details of these developments is told in the chapter about the Grumman E-2 Hawkeye family which follows. Even so, this was the most propitious step ever in AEW development, and it went largely unnoticed.

The E-2 was the only significant AEW programme with aircraft in build throughout the 1960s and it was the focal point of all US effort, but there was much to report from elsewhere. In Britain the planners got one hell of a fright when the E-2 was revealed. It was going to cost a lot to buy and there was a reluctance to sit so firmly on the lap of US technology. Even so, Royal Navy squadrons were due to get their first Buccaneers, and if there was anything else like it on the other side of the Iron Curtain, Britain was vulnerable. Far too vulnerable to be complacent.

The stalwarts, especially those connected with the drafting of Naval operational requirements issued a document which described what was wanted. It reached industry as Naval Air Specification 6166 in January, 1963. Simultaneously, a lot of promising research into the operation of a

new type of radar, called frequency-modulated intermittent continuous-wave (FMICW), which was still very embryonic, was nevertheless looking good. The airborne radar group at RRE, Great Malvern, was working in conjunction with Elliotts on this new concept and together they began to probe methods of using the FMICW technique in two particular roles. One was a fighter airborne-interception (AI) radar, and the other was an AEW surveillance radar.

Fleet protection was what troubled the Admiralty in Britain. Although the Gannet AEW.3 was a redoubtable little machine, it was hardly magnificent. So, as soon as the US Navy looked like stepping into a breathtaking lead, NAS 6166 was designed to put the whole thing into perspective.

The first ploy was to set a thief to catch a thief, in a roundabout sort of fashion. At a meeting held between Hawker Siddeley design personnel and Admiralty representatives on February 14, 1963, it was decided to proceed with the design of a Buccaneer-derivative which had two 4.6 × 0.6 m (15 × 2 ft) sideways-facing radar antennas in the bomb bay. The aircraft was to cruise at 38,000 ft, and detect targets all-round at heights between zero and 80,000 ft altitude at ranges of up to 250 nm.

The design team at Brough looked at a retractable antenna set, and even considered using an inflatable radome which would have blown out from beneath the aircraft like a huge bubble of chewing gum. The antennas reached 5.5 m (18 ft) in length, but at best only two 120°-wide arcs could be scanned. There was no radar coverage either fore or aft. By late 1963 the Brough team had reasoned that the Blue Parrot radar in the Buccaneer's nose would perhaps fill that gap, so why not put a radar in the tail too? They

The prototype Grumman E-2A Hawkeye, seen here on its first flight, October 21, 1960, was an aerodynamic shell. Later it was fitted with the first AMTI-radar, and that revolutionized AEW technology. Variants of the Hawkeye have been in production ever since, and seem set for a staggering 30 years, or more, production history

thought about dispensing with the sideways-facing antennas, but the RRE scientists told them it would need 3.05 to 3.66 m (10 to 12 ft) diameter scanners to achieve the range requirement. Someone drew a configuration, based on a Buccaneer fuselage, and its dumbbell-like outline was consigned to the waste-paper bin. That's a pity because it was probably the first time that a fore and aft scanner system (FASS) had been considered, anywhere. Britain was to become firmly convinced that the clear radar aperture provided by this type of installation made it far more preferable than the rotodome which Grumman had used for the E-2.

Late in 1963 the Admiralty returned to industry with the suggestion that a new aircraft might be considered. They envisaged buying four AEW aircraft for each carrier, but to boost the total production they wanted related airframes to do AEW and carrier on-board delivery (COD) duties. This was a chip off the E-2 block, as that programme had just spawned the Greyhound COD aircraft.

Meanwhile, the Admiralty planted the idea of using an HS.125 conversion, then a business-jet which had started flight-test and which had the potential to do COD and AEW tasks. A mushroom radome design with a 3.88 × 1.22 m (12.75 × 4 ft) antenna was drafted, but the radar specification—which amongst other things was now calling for heightfinding too—was too demanding to fit in such small aircraft. (Note that a mushroom is a stationary dorsal radome in which the scanner rotates, eg: Grumman Tracer, while a rotodome is a scanner/antenna combination that spins on its support). After this project, in 1964/1965, virtually all British AEW aircraft projects used the FASS installation.

Funds were put into antenna-sizing studies around early 1964. At the time the radar team was still trying to keep both the UK FMICW and the American AMTI options open, and they considered that elliptical scanners measuring 6.1 × 1.5 m (20 × 5 ft) or 4.9 × 1.2 m (16 × 4 ft), (which needed a mushroom or rotodome) or circular scanners 3.0 m (10 ft), 2.4 m (8 ft) or 1.8 m (6 ft) in diameter (which could have FASS installations) should bracket a set of workable possibilities. These dimensions were used on many subsequent projects.

The project which drew most attention was the Brough-designed P.139, which the chief designer saw fit to dub, for its portly proportions, 'the flying pig.' With radomes fore and aft enclosing 2.4 m (8 ft) diameter scanners (a variant with 3.0 m (10 ft) diameter antennas was also considered, but eventually dropped), this began to look like a possible AEW/COD aircraft. The carrier lifts on all projected UK carriers at the time

measured 15.2 × 6.1 m (50 × 20 ft), specifically to accomodate the Barnes Wallis-designed Swallow without any airframe hinges. The longer-than-usual lift length was welcome, but the narrow width was problematical. At some stages in the P.139 design process each of the five basic flying surfaces had a hinge: at such times it was worth thinking again!

The P.139 ended up as a T-tailed design, otherwise like a bulbous version of the Lockheed S-3A Viking, which came along at a later date. Power was to have been provided by two Rolls-Royce RB.172/T-260B engines, then only proposals, but later the engine used by the Anglo-French Jaguar. Windtunnel tests showed that drag was acceptable—although hardly minimal—but stability assessments showed there was no doubt that if it had ever been built Brough's P.139 would have resurrected an ancient Blackburn tradition (which the Buccaneer had skirted) of producing damned-awful-to-fly aircraft.

By 1965 the radar scientists were coming down very positively in favour of using FMICW. They had already advised the airframe people not to

A proposal considered by the British Admiralty in 1964 was a carrier-compatible version of the HS.125 business jet with a fixed dorsal radome

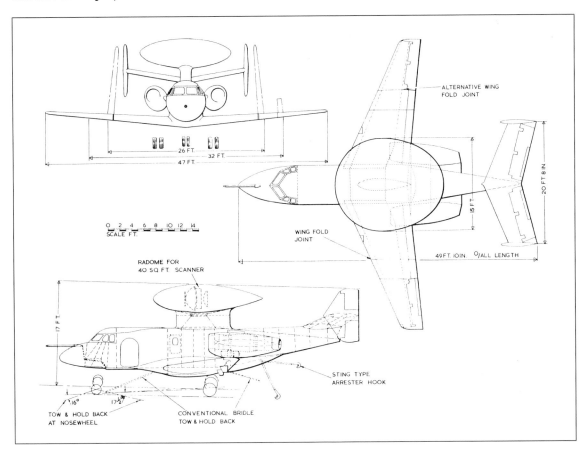

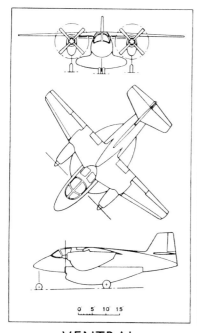

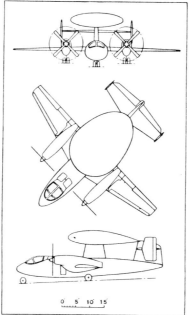

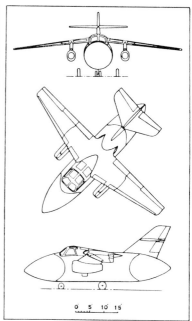

VENTRAL
16×4′ ELLIPTICAL DISH

MUSHROOM
16×4′ ELLIPTICAL DISH

FORE AND AFT
8′ DIAM DISH

British AEW project work began in early 1962 with a comparative study of several aircraft configurations. All were suitable for carrier-borne operations and designed to replace the Fairey Gannet AEW.3

When the P.139 configuration was frozen it had a high-set tail. The aircraft shape was driven by British insistence that fore-and-aft facing radar antennas should be used

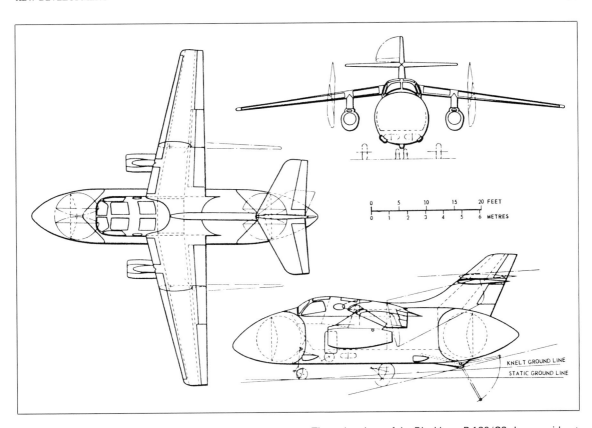

These drawings of the Blackburn P.139/C3 show a mid-set
tail version of a basic airframe which was proposed in 1963
in AEW/freighter/carrier-on-board delivery roles

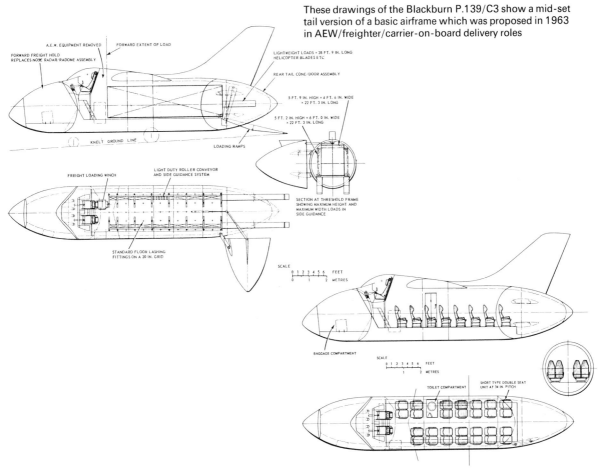

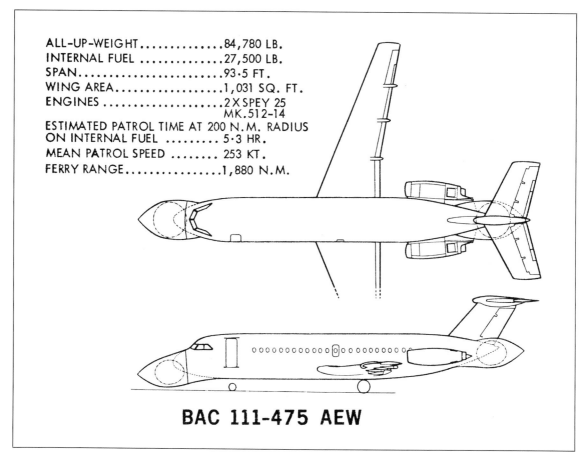

ALL-UP-WEIGHT..............84,780 LB.
INTERNAL FUEL ....27,500 LB.
SPAN.......................93·5 FT.
WING AREA..................1,031 SQ. FT.
ENGINES ....2×SPEY 25
                          MK.512-14
ESTIMATED PATROL TIME AT 200 N.M. RADIUS
ON INTERNAL FUEL .... 5·3 HR.
MEAN PATROL SPEED .... 253 KT.
FERRY RANGE...............1,880 N.M.

BAC 111-475 AEW

RAF requirements for a land-based AEW type elicited this
highly unlikely conversion of a BAC One-Eleven airliner

Hawker Siddeley at Hatfield proposed this AEW version of
the company's HS.144 feederliner project to meet RAF
operational requirements in the mid-sixties

mix turboprops with this type of radar, as the
whirling propellors would cause 'ghosting' in the
radar frequency-spectrum, but simultaneously
they advised that clutter-rejection problems
would ease considerably if the aircraft flew as
slowly as possible. The P.139 was optimized to
cruise at only 1.2 × stalling speed. British design
teams were also being told to consider the enclosure of inverted-cassegrain type antennas. There
was little doubt by then that the UK was going
to favour an FMICW, fore-and-aft inverted-cassegrain antenna configuration. It was a valiant
decision, and with only one significant departure
made en-route, an offspring managed to fly
through the red-tape fourteen years later.

At Hatfield there were attempts to make the
HS.144 feederliner project into an amenable
AEW type, while at Weybridge the BAC team
looked at VC-10s and One-Elevens, and so on.
But in 1965 the Labour government struck its

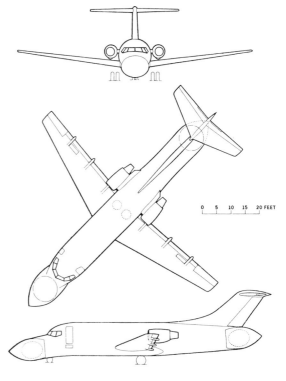

HS.144 SERIES 100 A.E.W. AIRCRAFT

mortal blow. As surely as TSR.2, P.1154, HS.681 and other aerospace projects went under the axe, so too did the UK carrier fleet. The pressure was relieved on the design of a carrier compatible AEW aircraft. It was a decision that was to have mortal consequences when the carrier fleet that was resurrected was tested in battle during the Falklands conflict in 1982.

Within the Air Ministry, soon to become a part of the Ministry of Defence (MoD), it was recognized by now that land-based AEW had to be developed, and as Britain strove to keep on the right side of Europe there was a period which saw Anglo-French AEW initiatives. The Breguet Atlantic was one of several aircraft which were considered to be potential carriers of the British FMICW radar, but this collaborative phase collapsed in a heap of conflicting requirements.

Brough was soon asked to look at a land-based AEW aircraft. The most suitable airframe was the then proposed HS.801 anti-submarine derivative of the Comet airliner, which is familiar today as the Nimrod. In a report prepared in August 1966 the illustration below was included. It was not until 1979 that an aircraft almost identical to that shown with 2.34 m (7.67 ft) diameter antennas was to fly, and to become Britain's AEW Nimrod. Even so, that did not preclude vacillations: those pecunious

characters at the Treasury thought that the 100 ton HS.801 proposal was far too big and expensive. (In fact, it was barely half the weight of the US E-3A Sentry which was on the drawing board to do the same job for the US Air Force.) An in-phrase at the time was that the UK aerospace

In 1966, when this model of an AEW Nimrod proposal was made, British industry was told to design a smaller and less expensive AEW aircraft—and then built the original aircraft over a decade later

BELOW A copy from a report submitted to the Ministry of Defence by Hawker Siddeley Brough in August 1966. The HS.801, now Nimrod, had still to fly, and it was another 11 years before an aircraft virtually identical to that shown second from bottom was funded

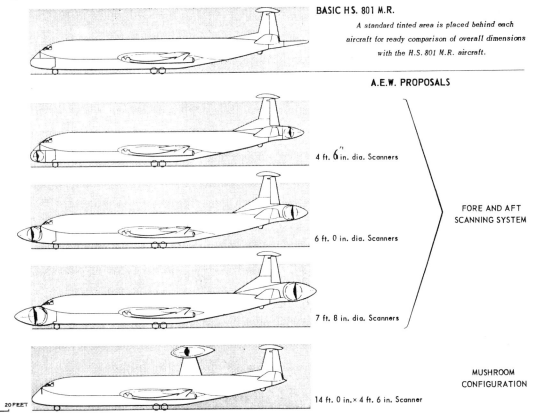

BASIC HS. 801 M.R.

A standard tinted area is placed behind each aircraft for ready comparison of overall dimensions with the H.S. 801 M.R. aircraft.

A.E.W. PROPOSALS

4 ft. 6 in. dia. Scanners

6 ft. 0 in. dia. Scanners

7 ft. 8 in. dia. Scanners

FORE AND AFT SCANNING SYSTEM

MUSHROOM CONFIGURATION

14 ft. 0 in. × 4 ft. 6 in. Scanner

0   10   20 FEET

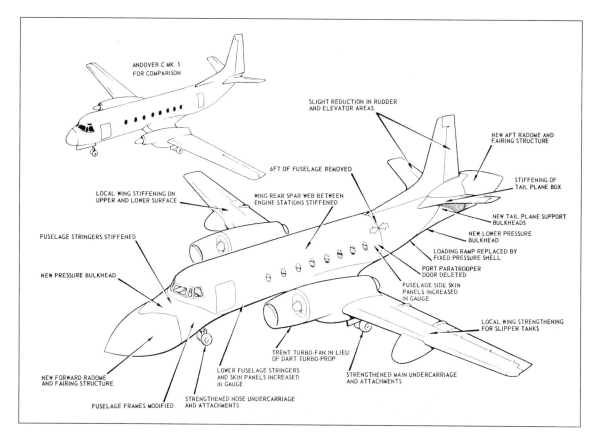

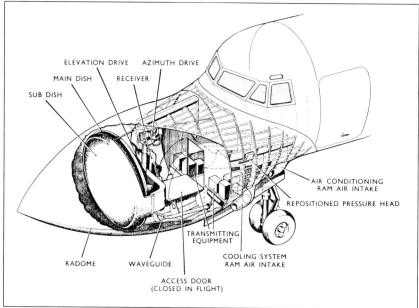

ELEVATION DRIVE   AZIMUTH DRIVE
MAIN DISH   RECEIVER
SUB DISH
                                        AIR CONDITIONING
                                        RAM AIR INTAKE
                                        REPOSITIONED PRESSURE HEAD
                        TRANSMITTING
                        EQUIPMENT
                        COOLING SYSTEM
                        RAM AIR INTAKE
RADOME   WAVEGUIDE
        ACCESS DOOR
        (CLOSED IN FLIGHT)

The HS Andover AEW is a hitherto unpublished project, and all design work was conducted at Brough between 1966 and 1967. It did not meet RAF patrol-duration requirements, and to the relief of all concerned the project was abandoned

industry was 'feather-bedded.' When one reflects on how sane design decisions were so highfalutingly disregarded, one has to confess that from the designer's point of view the feather bed was rather uncomfortable.

In 1967 the Hawker Siddeley team at Brough was told to start again, aiming to produce a smaller and cheaper land-based AEW type, and taking as its datum the HS Andover. Apparently, the slashes that were being applied to all military expenditure had left 15 Andover airframes ready for adaptation as AEW aircraft. The design that transpired was bizarre. The circular antennas proposed previously were compressed to an oval shape, measuring 2.4×1.8 m (8×6 ft) to provide ground clearance beneath the forward radome, otherwise the radar installation used in the original AEW Nimrod proposal was adopted. A picture shows that what else was done was hardly designed to make the aeroplane look beautiful. Rolls-Royce RB.203-1 Trent engines replaced the Dart turboprops, fuel tanks sprouted from beneath the wings, and no less than 1.8 m (6 ft) was chopped out of the aft fuselage. The grotesque forward radome looked like a Toucan's beak. Brough's chief designer, anxious to make it clear that he backed the FASS installation rather than a rotodome, seized upon this likeness, and many are the Air Staff representatives who can remember his finger pointing at the drawings as he said 'Toucan do the job better than one can!'

British paperwork effort came to an end at this point. The Andover-derivative (Toucan if you wish) was workable, but not man enough for the job. The radar boffins were flying a simple FMICW set in a Canberra in 1967, but that was more useful to the fighter radar development programme than to the AEW team, so they were allocated funds to produce a single-scanner system which could be installed on a Comet airframe. It would simulate the front portion of the AEW Nimrod FASS proposal.

In 1971 the trials Comet, XZ626, was in the Hawker Siddeley factory at Chester, the metalwork necessary to bolt the new radar on was ready, and the FMICW radar was physically two-thirds complete at Great Malvern. By that time the inevitable happened. The Treasury froze the funding. XZ626 was converted back to a standard Comet, the metalwork, radome and radar installation were put in storage at RRE and British AEW development was at an all-time low.

This may strike the reader as strange, for the UK had surely learned that AEW was essential. They had indeed, but the scientists had been hit across the nose by the Americans, yet again. In 1970 the US Air Force had ordered the Boeing E-3A into production. They were not having anything to do with FMICW radar for their aircraft. The US choice was pulse-Doppler radar, and now Britain was wondering if there really was a better horse to back.

The origins of pulse-Doppler radar have been discussed, at least in respect of their influence on operational requirements, in Chapter 4, and the operation of the system is described thoroughly in Chapter 3. The aim here must be to convey the significance of the two proposals that faced Britain's radar designers in 1971.

An FMICW radar uses radiation which changes frequency over a period of time, such that when plotted on a graph it forms a pattern similar to that shown on the diagram overleaf.

This model of the Andover AEW reveals the distinctive nose profile which won it the nick-name 'Toucan'

A land-based AEW system was eventually fully funded in 1977, when this heavily-modified Comet began flight tests with a representative nose radar

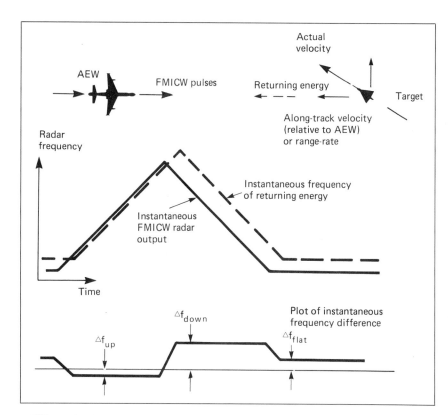

Frequency-Modulated Intermittent Continuous-Wave Radar

This illustration strictly shows a frequency-modulated/continuous wave radar. In an FMICW application it would be pulsed very rapidly, possibly in excess of a million times in the course of the period illustrated. Three frequency-modulation periods, as shown, are typical, and the 'triplet' of frequency differences between emitted and received radiation has characteristics related to both target range and range rate. It is a very difficult radar to jam, and it was proposed for early British AEW projects

When the frequency of energy which is returning to the radar is compared with that which is being emitted at the same instant it is found to vary. The combination of the three frequency differences (called a frequency-triplet) in each cycle of frequency variations can be decoded to reveal both range and range-rate. This description is only really true for an uninterrupted transmission (an FM/CW radar), and FMICW is a pulsed system, plagued with all the haromics created by PRF intervals, which are explored in depth in Chapter 3, in respect of pulse-Doppler applications. The underlying principals remain similar however, and the details of differences are of no immediate concern to complete the AEW story here.

When a technical audit is completed the points for and against FMICW radar technique, in an AEW application, are approximately (and very briefly) thus:

1 FMICW is less likely to be affected by any jamming activities undertaken by an adversary.
2 FMICW tends to perform best at the highest possible PRF settings, but this increases the number of range-ambiguities which have to be resolved. On a long-range radar this can be disadvantageous.
3 FMICW was preferred over pulse-Doppler around 1965 when high-speed digital processing was in its infancy, because the technique did not rely heavily on this technology. By 1970 the great progress made with digital processing technology on which

pulse-Doppler operations depended, made it look as if the latter would be cheaper to implement in the late 1970s and beyond.
4 FMICW had been a lighter solution than pulse-Doppler in comparative studies conducted in Britain in the 1960s, but the rapid development of micro-electronics had now eroded most of that advantage.

In 1975, when UK AEW development was reinstated, it was to be based on a pulse-Doppler radar, with a mixture of medium and low-PRF features. It is worth, in passing, to note that point (2) above is not so important to a shorter-range fighter radar, and point (1) is much more important. UK research into FMICW does not stand to be wasted therefore, because this type of radar is being used in the Tornado F.2 fighter.

Throughout the late 1960s, the value of British AEW capability was being eroded. A programme aiming to enhance it by adding an indigenously-designed AMTI receiver was started in 1970, as much as anything to keep together the team which had been involved with the Comet programme. Elliott Brothers, by now going through a series of mergers and later to become part of the Marconi Avionics Group within the GEC-Marconi empire, developed a digital AMTI which was fitted to all British-operated AN/APS-20 radar between 1972 and 1973. Although the radar was a shorter-wavelength, and therefore shorter-range unit, than the AN/

APS-120, which was then in production for the US Navy's Hawkeye, this brought the UK abreast of the best technology in AEW operations.

The twelve modified Shackleton AEW.2s were used to re-form RAF No 8 Squadron, at Kinloss, on 1 January 1972, and from that date they were to contribute to UK air defences and Nato surveillance of low-flying aircraft in the Eastern Atlantic. In 1972 the aircraft were between 15–20 years of age, and were expected to be replaced by 1978, but that was a highly optimistic piece of guesswork because a successor wasn't anywhere in sight. In 1981 the aircraft were still operating, but their numbers were reduced to six, four airframes having reached their fatigue life, and a further service life of typically five years was expected of the remainder. The aircraft continued to operate from Kinloss, and despite their age they still looked immaculate. In the remaining period of operations single aircraft deployed at monthly intervals to Keflavik, in Iceland, and occasionally to West Germany, presumably to monitor flying in the Baltic Sea area, as the AN/APS-20, even with an AMTI, was hardly a radar for overland operations.

The Shackleton installation used a 2.3 × 0.9 m (7.5 × 3 ft) antenna and could detect large targets at up to 100 nm range. Crew consisted of a pilot and co-pilot on the flight deck, radio and naviga-

Britain's only AEW systems experience up to the start of AEW Nimrod development was the addition of airborne moving-target indicator (AMTI) capability to US radars in RAF Shackletons and Royal Navy Gannets. The modified Shackleton AEW.2s remained in service until the advent of AEW Nimrod

tion operator to port and flight engineer to starboard aft of the flight deck, and three radar operators facing port further aft. The three controller positions were designated radar operator, AEW operator and tactical co-ordinator (Taco) locations. The Taco was the radar operator responsible for vectoring fighters to targets detected by the AEW radar. Typical sorties of 10 hours duration were flown, but Shackleton capability was well in excess of this figure.

By 1973 Britain was keeping abreast with the US, in the vanguard of AEW technology, but only just and was beginning to invest in the technology it would adopt in the AEW Nimrod programme. The US on the otherhand had the Grumman E-2 Hawkeye in service, and the Boeing E-3A Sentry in development. Soviet engineers, of whom little is known without a lot of conjecture, revealed the Tupolev Tu-126 Moss in the last few months of 1969, and seemed to be the only nation as determined as Britain and the US to develop an indigenous AEW capability. The story of how each of these four major programmes has developed is revealed in the following four chapters.

KEY **GRUMMAN E-2C HAWKEYE**

1 Pilot
2 Co-pilot
3 Radar/communications operators
4 Crew toilet
5 Radar equipment (transmitter and receiver)
6 Navigation equipment
7 Communications equipment
8 Passive-detection system antennas
9 Radar antennas
10 IFF antennas

11 Rotodome retraction mechanism
12 Cooling system
13 Power supplies
14 Allison T56-A-425 turboprops, each rated at 4910 shp (3661 kW)
15 Fuel tanks—standard tanks 5,625 kg (12,400 lb)
          optional tanks 8,980 kg (19,800 lb)

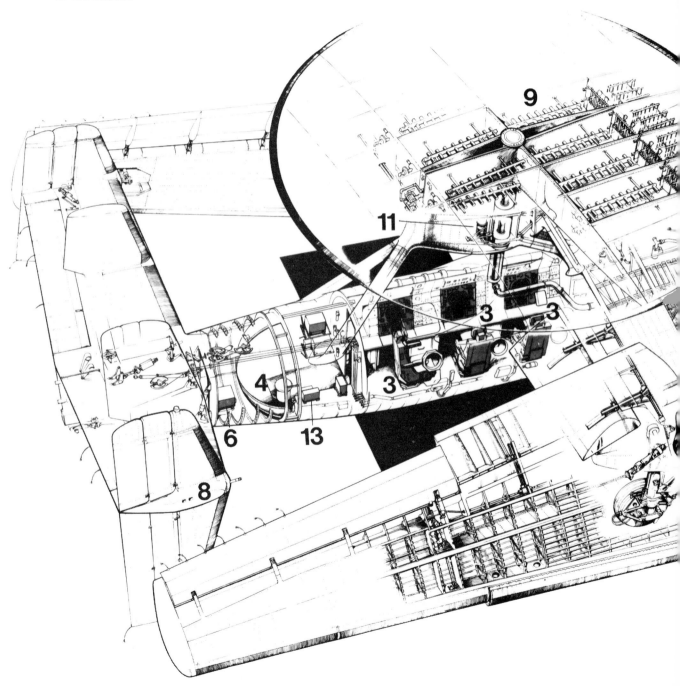

Chapter 7

Grumman E-2 Hawkeye

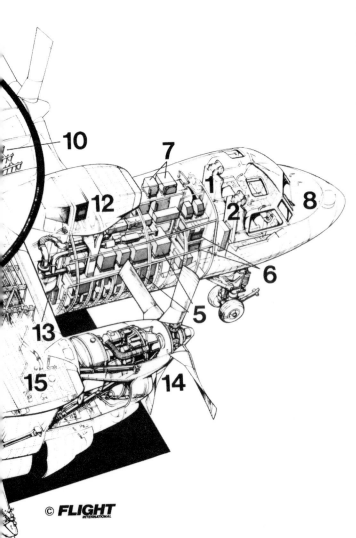

The US Navy launched the E-2 programme in 1959, when its latest AEW type, the WF-2 Tracer, had only just entered service. This early go-ahead was justified by inherent shortcomings in Tracer, and the urgent need for genuine long-range AEW performance.

Existing AEW aircraft could not really do what they ought to have been doing, and redressing the balance with a carrier-borne aircraft was a remarkable achievement. Earlier operations had relied almost entirely on the General Electric AN/APS-20 radar, and although improvements throughout its operational life were considerable, the radar fell a long way short of perfection. Early versions of the AN/APS-20 used a 1.8 m (6 ft) wide scanner, operated at S-band frequencies (2 to 4 GHz) and were relatively unaffected by meteorological conditions, provided they could be lifted above the weather. Detection range against a low-flying strike aircraft of the sort that would have threatened an aircraft carrier in the 1950s was a little better than 50 nm under favourable radar-viewing conditions. When seas were choppy, and assuming that whatever carried the radar could be launched and recovered under such sea conditions, there was the possibility that an intruder would get much closer before it was detected. It was better than nothing, but it wasn't brilliant. It would be unfair not to stress that later models of the radar, entering service almost concurrently with the Hawkeye's launch had almost twice this performance.

The WF-2 Tracer used the same radar—but repackaged by Hazeltine and designated AN/APS-82. It could see much further with its 4.27 m (14 ft) wide scanner, although some of the potential performance gain was discounted against improved reliability. For example, the magnetron was operated at only 50 per cent of the original maximum rated power output. Target-detection performance was probably 80 per cent better than an early AN/APS-20 under similar circumstances. Favourable conditions yielded a fair probability of seeing an attacker at 90 nm or so from the aircraft.

A cursory analysis reveals how opinion was

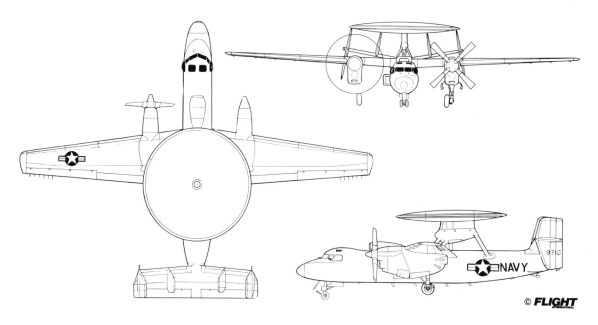

GRUMMAN E-2C HAWKEYE

Span	24.56 m (80 ft 7 in)
Length	17.55 m (57 ft 7 in)
Max height	5.59 m (18 ft 4 in)
Max gross wt	23,541 kg (51,900 lb)
Max level speed	325 knots
Cruise speed/altitude	270 knots/30,000 ft
Take-off distance	580 m (1900 ft)

Patrol performance   4 hours at 170 nm from base

Note: extra fuel increases max gross wt to 27,161 kg (59,880 lb) and increases patrol time by two hours

scaled around 1958: if a Tracer was overhead its carrier when it detected a threat, and an interceptor was already on deck, crew strapped-in, and launched within three minutes, a target approaching at 400 kt would have covered 20 nm from initial detection to the interceptor climbing away from the flight-deck. There would be a chance of the launched aircraft engaging the attacker at 30–40 nm from the ship. If there was more than one attacker, the chances of stopping the whole raid were stacked heavily against the ship. It probably could not launch enough aircraft, in sufficiently short time, to catch them all at a safe range.

The situation could be eased by having fighters on patrol, or by positioning the Tracer further out, but in the late-1950s the endurance of most front-line jet types was cruelly deficient. They sucked fuel abominably, and the frequency at which buddy-packed aircraft had to launch to top-up a returning aircraft or a 'bolter' was alarming by modern standards. Any chance of seeing the enemy just a little bit further away was clearly worth a lot to the US Navy.

Consider what General Electric's radar team had been uncovering during its research in the late-1950s. Their initial assessment pointed to a radar fitted with a pulse-compression system,

similar to that used to improve the resolution of ground-based radars. Operating over sea-states equivalent to the worst under which it felt aircraft could be reasonably launched and recovered, and compared with the AN/APS-82, they reckoned they could double the detection range against a given target!

The price of this progress was that 'look-down' capability against low-flying targets became extremely difficult at long-range, even with the UHF wavelength radiation that was postulated. Once the pulse-compression system had been analysed, the General Electric team was told to consider using non-coherent MTI techniques to solve the long-range detection problem.

They paused—and reflected on how they could squeeze what was already proven in ground-based radars into a small carrier-based aircraft. By early 1959 they were reasonably optimistic. Clearly the US Navy had its own scientists monitoring every assumption made, but even today it is not clear whether the people involved were all genuinely confident, or whether the US Navy simply believed that somehow it could be made to work—and it had to be made to work.

A full-scale aircraft and system development programme was authorized in 1959. There must have been many long nights of nervous pencil-chewing by a lot of the senior personnel, because it was undoubtedly a bold step and a very big gamble. The odds against success were high enough to discourage competition from anywhere else in the world.

Grumman was teamed with General Electric, and although many other companies co-operated there can be no denying that the US Navy's AEW future was committed to the competence of these two firms. In joint studies throughout the late 1950s the shape of a new aircraft had begun to make sense to both teams. General Electric had chosen to use an array of 12 Yagi antennas, and with Grumman's engineers they developed a slender saucer-shaped circular radome, 7.3 m (24 ft) in diameter. Scanning the Yagi-array to provide 360° coverage was felt to be best achieved by turning the whole radome; so the first rotodome to enter production was designed. Airframe blanking was deemed to be something that the teams could live with on such a long-range radar.

It would be intriguing to know how bargaining progressed in the design team, for the allocation of radar equipment mass and volume. General Electric was held to difficult mass objectives set by US Navy staff, and it is quite clear that Grumman would have not devoted any more of the airframe mass or volume than was absolutely necessary to the radar, because its objectives, set again by US Navy staff, was to produce an aircraft small enough to fit on an aircraft carrier, to cruise for four hours or more at over 200 nm from home, and to accommodate a vast amount of crew and equipment.

The Hawkeye's fuselage is a circular pressurised tube. At the front it blooms upwards to provide the flight-deck crew, just a pilot and a co-pilot, with reasonable headroom and a good view forward. Aft of the flight deck, and either side of a corridor designed for slim crewmen only, are racks of electronic equipment extending along 3.35 m (11 ft) of the fuselage length. Behind these, seated to face their consoles on the port side of the fuselage are the three system operators, and aft of them the fuselage truncates quite abruptly, after giving room for a crew toilet (users share it with a not inconsiderable number

Grumman was the most experienced of all AEW aircraft builders by the late fifties, when the WF-2 Tracer entered service with the US Navy. Although this type was soon to be eclipsed by the Hawkeye, the configuration was very influential on the newer aircraft

An E-2C comes into land with flaps down, ailerons drooping, hook and gear extended

TOP LEFT This early E-2A Hawkeye shows its bluff nose (with a non-standard instrumental boom), slim radome, and quartuplet fins

BOTTOM LEFT In striving to get efficient cruise performance, Grumman used a high aspect-ratio wing and a lift-generating rotodome, which needs de-icing protection around the rim. This is an E-2C from USS *Constellation*

of electronic boxes) and a bristling of external antennas.

Both the tailplane and the wing are attached to the top of the fuselage, with the wing box forming the cabin roof between the operator's quarters and the electronics racks. Above here the rotodome is attached, but it is not as simple as on any other aircraft. Ideally the radar antenna should be well above the fuselage and engine propellors, but the Grumman engineers wanted it lower to fit in a 5.55 m (18 ft) high hangar. They soon discovered that as they reduced rotodome clearance angry cries in the General Electric radar camp increased in proportion to the inverse-square (or would it have been the inverse fourth-power for a radar team?) of the rotodome-to-fuselage separation. It was shown by the radar engineers that the minimum acceptable rotodome separation in flight was 0.66 m (1.9 ft)

above the maximum height that the aircraft engineers had available for the aircraft to be trundled into a carrier hangar. Grumman had to arrange an elaborate pedestal of struts supporting an aerodynamically-contoured box in which hydraulics lift and lock the 910 kg (2000 lb) rotodome before each flight.

The wings are as high in aspect ratio as Grumman could contemplate, to obtain reasonable cruise efficiency. Outboard of the centre-section box each wing folds aft when on the carrier, and just inboard of the hinges on each side is the most grotesque nacelle ever designed for a turboprop. Even so, like the fuselage, it is a triumph that the practically-minded might study enviously. Each nacelle accommodates an Allison T56-A-425 turboprop engine, rated at 4910 eshp, and beneath it a stumpy main-gear leg with a single mainwheel. The retraction sequence calls for each leg to swing forward and twist, laying the mainwheels flat beneath the engine jetpipes. Each nacelle is about the same depth as the fuselage.

Finally, each tailplane is canted upwards 11°, and in addition to fins at the tips, which extend further below the tailplane than above it, there are two subsidiary fins at mid-span on the upper surface on each side. The four fins deserve some

Halted by the tug of arrestor gear an E-2C arrives back on deck

Taxying across the deck this E-2C has folded its wings. The rotodome will be lowered later to reduce overall height so that the aircraft can go below deck

attention by those who like to remember the unusual. Only three of the vertical surfaces have rudders: the odd-man out is the port inner fin. The rudders are also well below the size that the designers might have liked and use double hinges to increase their effectiveness.

The aircraft is 17.55 m (57.58 ft) long and has a span of 24.56 m (80.58 ft). A couple of comparative facts will help to put the E-2 into perspective. Take-off weight can be 23,540 kg (51,900 lb), or 27,160 kg (59,880 lb) if wet outer wing panels are used, which is about as hefty as a 60-seat turboprop airliner, and the Hawkeye packs a little short of 10,000 eshp into its two power units, which is more than is installed in a four-engined, 70–80 seat, Viscount airliner. Fuel capacity is fairly modest, amounting to only 3452 lit (912 US gal) per wing, and is all inboard of the hinge line, but is sufficient to give a ferry range of 1390 nm (2580 km). Optional tanks can be added outboard for land-based operations at the higher gross weight, total fuel capacity being boosted from 5625 kg (12,400 lb) to 8980 kg (19,800 lb).

Despite the tremendous design challenge, after go-ahead on 5 March 1959, the first flight of an aerodynamically-representative aircraft took place on 21 October 1960. The second aircraft, with a set of electronics on-board, first flew on 19 April 1961.

E-2 Hawkeye handling has never been criticized, but this is probably because of a lot of fine-tuning by the development team. The rotodome was supposed to be inclined to the local airstream such that it would generate a large proportion of the total aircraft lift, and to increase its lifting capability a relatively sharp-edged profile, with a circular de-icing boot around the rim, was selected. In service, however, Hawkeye always cruises with its large Fowler flaps extended by 10°, which does a lot to destroy rotodome lift. This procedure suggests that the rotodome might at first have generated so much lift that it destabilized the aircraft, and that an angle of attack (AOA) limit has to be strictly observed on the aircraft. Altogether this is a swings and roundabouts story. The rotodome is acknowledged to generate sufficient lift to offset its own mass, yet the aircraft now cruises in a slightly nose-down attitude, thereby reducing the range at which air-

frame blanking over the nose will extend. There must lurk, however, a drag penalty associated with the flap extension.

A final point about the aircraft's handling. Because vertical radar beam adjustments cannot be made to keep the radiation pattern horizontal when the aircraft is turning, flat turns have to be executed. This means that the pilot skids the aircraft around the turn at each end of his patrol pattern, using rudder and aileron in opposition so that the wings remain level and the nose slices across the horizon. Anyone who has ever flown an unco-ordinated turn like this will know how uncomfortable it can be. It can be especially nauseating for the system operators, who sit sideways and have no external reference. This is something that crews report they learn to live with after a few flights, but if you ever see a Hawkeye crewman going aboard with a coffee cup with a

A glimpse of an E-2C in build at Bethpage provides an impression of its size and complexity. ABOVE The rotodome is being shifted into position

LEFT This close-up shows the aircraft with the rotodome installed, and the pylon retraction flaps open. The extent to which the rotodome is lowered is clearly discernible

RIGHT Engineers check the variable-pitch mechanism on a new Hawkeye propellor. This four-bladed Hamilton Standard assembly takes the strain of almost 5000 eshp, and is all the more remarkable for being a predominantly glassfibre unit so that it does not interfere with radar operation

lid on top, you now know the reason why.

But these little discomfortures should be tucked away when assessing the Hawkeye's AEW performance. It was an astonishingly ambitious programme which happens to have left a few lessons for everyone to appreciate. The greatest pacing factor in the whole E-2 programme has been the radar system, and its development provides a convenient thread through successive generations of Hawkeye development.

Facts about the radar's capability are not easy to find, but the relative improvements attributable to the four metamorphoses passed through in about 15 years can be catalogued and put into perspective with the remainder of E-2 systems. The initial radar was called AN/APS-96, and was superseded around 1964 by the AN/APS-111, which in turn was modified to become the AN/APS-120 in aircraft delivered after 1971. The latter was the standard radar for the early E-2C Hawkeyes, but eventually it was superseded too, by the AN/APS-125 from about 1976. There is still sufficient work going on to warrant a further new designation in due course, but already the radar has been developed beyond the dreams that floated-out of General Electric's Utica project office in the late-1950s.

First, the AN/APS-96. This was the first AEW radar to operate in the UHF waveband (the actual frequency is classified, but antenna geometry suggests 400 MHz). It used a klystron transmitter which can be comparatively efficient at UHF wavelengths, and the operating principle was that of a low-PRF set: that is, reflected energy from the most distant target was received before the next pulse was transmitted. To get a sizeable amount of radiation per pulse without having to push the peak-power output level too high, long pulses were used. Long pulses are disadvantageous in one other respect however. The longer the pulse, the more uncertain the reflection range becomes. Range resolution can be improved if shorter pulses are used, and in the AN/APS-96, by using a delay-line system for pulse-compression, range resolution was restored synthetically. This technique is common today, but it was a significant first for this particular radar.

Long wavelength radiation tends to spread more readily than short wavelength radiation, forming sidelobes, and this was one reason for having an array of small antennas in as large a rotodome as possible. Even so, there would be little support in favour of a multiple-Yagi array in a radar designed today, as its sidelobe performance cannot hope to compare with the slotted

waveguide or inverted-cassegrain antennas which came along later. All things considered, the bearing and range resolution of the AN/APS-96 was equal to—or better than—the best variants of the AN/APS-20, and it could see right out to 200 nm or more, making it worthwhile to cruise the aircraft at 30,000 ft. Comparatively, the AN/APS-96 provided the same probability of detection of any particular target at approximately three or four times the ranges of the best AN/APS-20, or twice the range of the AN/APS-82. The latter had been introduced into service in 1959 aboard the WF-2 Tracer. It is hardly surprising that after only two years in production the Tracer was superseded by Hawkeyes on the Bethpage production line. The US Navy had a winner, yet remarkably there were still more rabbits to be pulled out of the hat.

AN/APS-111, which was introduced in later production E-2As, and eventually fitted to the whole fleet, was significant in being the first airborne radar to use non-coherent moving target indication (MTI), which from the nomenclature adopted on this programme became known universally as airborne-MTI (AMTI). The system was fairly simple, and it looked for beat frequencies—like the low frequency humming that can be caused by slightly unsynchronized propellors on a multi-engined aircraft. These frequencies are created in returning energy by objects which are moving relative to one another.

When a radar looks down from an aircraft, if the energy reflects directly from land or sea there will be a slight change in frequency due to Doppler shift, induced by the relative aircraft motion, but that is all. This should *not* be detectable by the beat-frequency filters in an AMTI system. Instead it has to find lower-frequency beating in banks of frequency-filters, which are rather temperamental pieces of equipment, prone to drift as they warm-up or as power-supply voltages vary. Enclosing the number of filters that were necessary in the AN/APS-111 in a few cubic feet, while at the same time ensuring that any heat generated was conducted away, was a problem that many observers had steadfastly refused to believe could be beaten—but it was.

With the AN/APS-111, except when the most atrocious sea-states were running, and in a few roguish instances, aircraft and ships were identifiable, and their bearing and range determinable at distances of up to 200 nm. Small aircraft and small ships could not be detected with any fair probability until they were closer, but even so there was enough information coming back from the radar for operators to soon fill their screens

DANGER
RESTRICTED
AREA

with china-graph pencil marks. In fact, here was a ludicrous dichotomy. The radar was so efficient that without a good information-filter between it and the crew, the amount of data generated could swamp the operators. That was a serious problem, and it had to be solved fast. We will return to looking at how the radar was further developed after the solution to the operator's dilemma has been outlined.

The Hawkeye rotodome also had an IFF interrogation set installed. This was invaluable for friendly aircraft identification and in the E-2A an automatic data-correlation system, comprising some rather cumbersome processing technology, including a magnetic-drum memory that did not take kindly to the environment in an AEW aircraft, was supposed to carry-out the more laborious identification tasks. The data system was never meant to be subjected to so much abuse during continuous operation, and frequent failures forced the operators to keep abreast of raw data being fed in from both radar and IFF. This could amount to many dozens of targets, even in excess of 100 in peak periods, and yet tests with air traffic controllers in similar situations have shown that their decision-making abilities are considerably impaired if they have to watch more

A batch of three new E-2Cs await delivery from Bethpage

than 12 aircraft simultaneously. On E-2As the situation was obviously desperate, and never more so than when the aircraft could be most valuable because of the vast amount of traffic about. To help solve this problem the E-2 family received its first digital computer in the late-1960s. This was a Litton L-304 general-purpose unit, and it replaced the original magnetic-drum memory and analogue track-correlation hardware.

Several airframe modifications were introduced at the same time, the most noticeable external difference being a slight enlargement of the fins. All aircraft were given the new features by 1971, and re-designated E-2B Hawkeye. They were aerodynamically superior to the E-2A—aircrews found flying characteristics just a little sweeter, and radar tracking became a lot easier for the operators.

The E-2A's history was quite short because of this extensive modification programme. First deliveries had taken place on 19 April 1964 to VAW-111 at San Diego. Operational flying commenced in 1965 on the USS *Kitty Hawk* (CVA-63) and the USS *Ranger* (CVA-61), which were both operating in South-East Asia, and so gave the E-2A a quick introduction to real wartime operations. By 1967 the US Navy had taken delivery of its full quota of 59 E-2As. Detachments were operational on the USS *Constellation* (CVA-64), USS *Coral Sea* (CVA-43) and USS *Enterprise* (CVAN-65). On several carriers Hawkeye was used alongside Tracer, and there was simply no comparison. Tracer was removed from the carriers! All carrier-based aircraft in the Fleet were now turbine-powered, and this allowed the US Navy to standardize on jet-fuel.

Of the 59 E-2As delivered, 52 were converted to E-2B standard by 1971. Two of the original aircraft were designated TE-2A and used for conversion training, and at least one aircraft was held back to conduct further radar development

flying. The four aircraft unaccounted for were presumably lost during the six years of E-2A operations.

For all that the rudimentary AMTI capability in the E-2B AN/APS-111 radar was streets ahead of what was available anywhere else in the world, the US Navy was still keen to tackle some requirements that remained outstanding. For example, the E-2B was not particularly good when it was operated near to landmasses, as the AMTI often failed to recognize aircraft against the specular clutter. In some cases aircraft could

Hawkeye crewmen have small workspaces. In the fuselage they sit sideways with no external view, and have to endure the discomfort of skidding turns. The operator in the foreground is using a light pen to transfer data on his displays

flit between islands and remain undetected (that was happening in the Mediterranean) or disappear against the background provided by a swampy landscape (and that was happening around Vietnam). It is important to bear in mind that these shortcomings were being seen around 1965, when Grumman had just started delivery of the A-6 Intruder to the US Navy, and the Navy was therefore well placed to assess fleet vulnerability to such threats. It was also at the time when Britain was just beginning to put together its own ideas on how the conduct AEW effectively overland and overwater, and the US Air Force had recently started on its Overland Radar Technology (ORT) research programme, which would not lead to a mature overland AEW being operational for another 12 years. When General Electric was instructed to add overland detection capability to the AN/APS-111 it was therefore a bold step both in respect of using what technology was available, and in integrating it with the radar which was already available.

The result was a new radar, called AN/APS-120. The rotodome remained essentially unchanged, but it was now matched with a much improved radar transmitter (rated at 1 Mw peak power output) and new receiver equipment. Exactly what goes on in the receiver is something that the US Navy, even today, is determined to keep to itself. All that can be said is that it remained a predominantly-analogue system and it embodied what was, in its time, a very comprehensive frequency-analyzer facility. To meet the necessary frequency-discrimination requirements called for a lot of separate frequency-filters, and fitting these into the E-2 was not necessarily in line with another US Navy requirement; that the radar should be made easier to maintain. Nevertheless, the performance claims, and subsequent production history of this airframe/radar combination, leave no doubt that this task was completed successfully.

Putting a frequency-sensitive radar into a turboprop-powered aircraft is one way of living dangerously. The basic problem of the turboprop is that many frequencies within the waveband of interest to the radar engineer can be induced by the flicker of propellor blades in the radar's field-of-view. To minimise this effect Hamilton-Standard had already produced a four-bladed propellor which used a steel spar embedded in each blade and surrounded by plastic foam with a glassfibre skin. Remembering that the 4.1 m (13.5 ft) diameter propellor transmits 4910 eshp at maximum rating, and the relative infancy of glassfibre applications, the engineering effort involved was exceptional. Grumman had also used glassfibre material extensively in the aircraft fins, and again the basic premise was to minimize radar interference.

Conversion of an E-2A airframe, incorporating all the new features of the radar, began in June 1965 and was completed in time for first flight in October 1967. Immediately the results showed how well the new AN/APS-120 radar was operating, and the US Navy began to draw up plans to operate a new Hawkeye variant with the radar from Naval Air Stations on the US East Seaboard. The production plans were authorized in May 1968, and the aircraft designated E-2C Hawkeye. The first of two pre-production aircraft flew on 20 January 1971, and the first production airframe flew on 23 September 1972. E-2C production has remained steady ever since, making it the most numerous and most widely-used AEW aircraft in the world.

The US Navy again completely revised the system fit in the third major Hawkeye variant. Its requirements called for the E-2C to be capable of both active and passive target detection, automatic tracking of many targets simultaneously (250 initially), and multiple interception control. As commented already the radar was now the AN/APS-120, and the rotodome, although still basically similar to predecessors was designated AN/APN-171, and produced by Randtron. The radar system was complemented by a Hazeltine RT-988 IFF interrogator and a Litton AN/ALR-73 passive-detection system (PDS).

The latter was a significant addition, and has become a standard feature of all new Hawkeyes. Four sets of aerials, each comprising four separate spiral antennas, are installed in the extremities of the fuselage and at each tailplane tip. They provide 360° coverage over an extremely wide band of frequencies, and can detect the emissions associated with raiders beyond ranges at which radar might detect the targets using them. A small compensation for the installation of this system is a 0.53 m (1.75 ft) nose extension which added some grace to the blunt nose of the E-2A/B. All PDS data is fed to a general-purpose digital computer where information such as frequency, pulsewidth, PRF and distance is analyzed. Data is compared with stored information to sift-out irrelevant electronic activity, and in some cases an indication of enemy threat identities is possible. The Litton processor used for this task initially had a re-loadable store so that threat data pertinent to the operations could be loaded before each flight. Computational capability was many times greater than the central processor which was used in the E-2B Hawkeye. Even so, the PDS processor is eclipsed by the staggering capability of the E-2C's central processor.

At the time of writing the E-2C had been in production for about ten years, and it's central processor had been improved upon several times. The acknowledged core of the on-board data-processor is a Litton OL-77/ASQ unit. This started life in 1972 as two L-304 computers with eight 8192 word memory modules, to which about 50 per cent extra capacity had been added by 1982, and a move to double the original capacity was being contemplated. Automatic tracking of 250 targets initially has been extended to more than 600, and at any time automatic control of more than 40 intercepts and strike missions is claimed. This capability suggests use of a much larger capacity and faster computer than is generally credited.

The operator's positions are now customized to the following primary roles: air controller at the rear, combat information officer in the centre and radar operator at the front. Each operator has a Hazeltine AN/APA-172 console which provides two display surfaces. The main display is a 25 cm (10 in) diameter plan-position indicator on which sensor information can be presented in a pictorial format. The operator can indicate any target by pointing a light-pen at its position on the tube. The central computer seeks information on the specified target in its track-library and writes the details on a small 13 cm (5 in) diameter alpha-numeric display.

There is insufficient room to have a full stand-by crew, or any real crew-rest facilities. A spare seat is available for crew rotation, although typical missions of 6 hours duration are flown, and even up to 9 hours for land-based aircraft with extra fuel capacity.

Information passes to and from the aircraft by a comprehensive set of communication equipment which comprises the tactical data system (TDS). It uses datalink and is largely configured to feed data to a common operations centre (COC), which would normally be a seaborne vessel. Nevertheless there are also facilities for direct communication with aircraft involved in missions which the AEW type is monitoring.

In addition to the sensor, processing and communication equipment, the aircraft also carries a respectable selection of navigation and guidance systems. The main navigation references are a Litton AN/ASN-92 carrier-aircraft inertial navigation set (Cains), a Lear-Siegler AN/ASN-50 attitude and heading reference system, and a General Precision AN/APN-152 Doppler navigation radar set. Data from these are combined with the outputs from a Conrac CP-1085/A air-data computer and can provide position and flightpath information to the crew on conventional instruments, or directly to other equipment. The operator's receive flightpath data automatically to stabilize and orientate sensor information, and the Sperry AN/ASW-15 automatic flight control system can use flightpath data to fly automatic patrol patterns. An AN/ASW-25B automatic carrier landing system is also fitted and standard radio navaids include an ITT AN/APN-52(V) Tacan set, Collins ARA-50 ADF receiver and Honeywell AN/APN-171(V) radio altimeter. Of little direct interest to the aircrew, but vital for speedy turnaround and maintenance, is a flight performance monitoring system which logs all equipment unservicabilities.

External changes, in addition to the nose extension which accommodates the PDS antenna, include an extra bulge on top of the fuselage to accommodate a 0.74 m² (8 ft²) vapour-cycle condenser. This is additional to a slightly smaller unit strapped to the starboard side of the fuselage of all models, and is no doubt essential to maintain an even temperature in the avionic bays. Good cooling performance can be reflected in increased equipment reliability, and mission reliability figures in excess of 95 per cent are reported frequently in E-2C brochures. This is a target that would have only been achievable after much painstaking development.

The US Navy initially ordered 28 E-2C Hawkeyes, with production scheduled between 1971 and 1975. All the aircraft were to be operated by US East Coast Squadrons, complementing 44 E-2Bs on US West Coast Squadrons. The first E-2C was delivered to the US Navy in December 1971, and the type entered service with VAW-123, at Norfolk NAS, Virginia, in November the following year. In September 1974 E-2Cs were operated from carriers for the first time when USS *Saratoga* was on duty in the Mediterranean.

Subsequently, as the E-2B fleet began to show signs of decay, the US Navy decided to trust E-2C to handle all its AEW operations. Production has continued following the initial batch of 28 aircraft at about 6 aircraft per year, and the delivery schedule calls for the 84th E-2C to be delivered in 1984, by which time almost all the E-2Bs will have been phased-out. Further order extensions are likely take total US Navy E-2C procurement past the 100 mark.

The additional aircraft are being produced with an even more impressive radar than the ear-

lier E-2C models. The AN/APS-125 represents virtually the ultimate stage to which a radar with an ancestry right back to the early sixties can be developed. The official description of what the radar can achieve has hardly been amplified in any publicly-released information. It simply states that 'an advanced radar processing system (ARPS) automatically detects air and sea targets overwater and overland. Fighter size aircraft are detected at ranges in excess of 200 nm, while larger, bomber-sized targets are detected to the limits of radar range. Smaller targets, such as cruise missiles, can be detected at ranges in excess of 125 nm. In actual operations the E-2C has detected small patrol boats at over 100 nm. The ARPS also incorporates electronic counter-countermeasure (ECCM) technology . . .'. Official literature refers to the radar using a digital AMTI processor, and in some circles it is often referred to as a pseudo pulse-Doppler system.

The main features of the radar are dimly visible in the framework of the text. From its origins as a simple pulse-compression analogue radar (around 1960), the system had become, by 1976, a sizeable digital system with many of the basic elements of a pulse-Doppler radar in its receiver hardware. Its antenna, it has to be admit-

Grumman F-14 Tomcat, laden with six Phoenix long-range air-to-air missiles, is the E-2C's stablemate in production, and with Hawkeye is the heart of the current US Navy fleet-protection system

ted, is not the best for the job, but it seems to have been skilfully developed so that it is adequate. But US Navy technicians dread the replacement of any Yagi element, because re-harmonizing the whole array is a time-consuming process.

It is hardly surprising to know that antenna development is still given some priority in US Navy budgets. Randtron, at the time of writing, had revealed a few details of a new antenna called TRAC-A. It promises to have lower sidelobes than the existing design, but uses the same configuration as the existing multi-Yagi AN/APN-171 system, and if it were ever introduced on service aircraft the change would only be noticeable to anyone trying to jam the radar emissions. Their job would be a bit more difficult than before.

A testimony to the E-2Cs capability, and relatively low price tag, which is speculated to be around $40 million, has been its adoption by other services. At least four E-2Cs are operated by the Israeli air force, and the first aircraft of eight on order have entered service with the Japanese Air Self-Defence Force. Japan may buy more. Both Egypt and Singapore announced orders for Hawkeye in 1983, and there are many pointers suggesting that an order will be placed by France. A US Navy aircraft was evaluated at Mont de Marsau by the French air force in June 1980, and this could have stimulated an actual order by the time this book is published. Interest has also been expressed by Australia, which one can understand, and by Switzerland, which is surprising.

E-2C operators, and their operations, are covered in more detail in a later chapter, but the nature of their missions when operating with a fleet at sea is in many ways more demanding than land-based AEW aircraft operations. Crews, after being catapulted off the carrier, are expected to zig-zag about at low-level—if they climbed immediately and were detected by an enemy AEW the ship's position would be evident. Recovery, for the same reason, is often as clandestine too. Typically an E-2C will patrol no more than 200 nm from its carrier or shore base, at about 29,000 ft, cruising at 260 kt for 4 hours.

A postscript to the E-2C Hawkeye tale deals with its success in 73 operations off Florida in October–December 1981. In conjunction with US Coast Guard operations Hawkeyes led to the arrest of 97 persons accused of drug-smuggling. Operation Thunderbolt caught 45 aircraft, 7 vessels and 12,242 kg (26,983 lb) of marijuana. Grumman had even issued a press release saying that the Hawkeyes were operating off the coast of Florida, so one might wonder why the smugglers were caught napping. The fact is that the official explanation for having Hawkeyes off Florida was to monitor the second launch of the US Space Shuttle from Cape Canaveral. Officialdom gets some knocks in this book for its blunderings, but in this case it proved, undeniably, that it also has a wry sense of humour.

In 1981 E-2C Hawkeyes, including this example from USS *Forrestal*, were based in Florida to track a Space Shuttle launch. They managed also to catch a record crop of drug smugglers who tried to creep into the US in ships and aircraft during that period

Chapter 8
Boeing E-3 Sentry

With its appetite for a comprehensive AEW type whetted by the limited capability of the Lockheed EC-121s, which were operated from the mid-1950s, the US Air Force watched radar developments closely throughout the late fifties and early sixties. The AMTI concept which had spurred the US Navy into E-2 Hawkeye development around 1959 was not so attractive to the Air Force, which was intent on overland intruder detection. Although AMTI showed promise overwater, it was not ideal overland. However, in the early 1960s electronic technology entered into the era of miniaturization. Long-range pulse-Doppler radar would soon be feasible, and with good overland performance. It should be noted that pulse-Doppler techniques were already used on production radars, but the electronics used were analogue and rudimentary. The radars were also short-range units. It was not a simple matter of scaling up these applications for a long-range overland radar.

In 1963 the US Air Force Electronic Systems Division, looked ahead optimistically, and started its Overland Radar Technology (ORT) programme, which aimed to determine what technology would be necessary to make long-range pulse-Doppler work, whether it was likely to be achieved in the coming decade, and in what way it could be adopted for military 'look-down' operations. AEW applications were given priority and three research radars were tested in an EC-121. In these tests the aircraft's lower radome accommodated the first slotted-waveguide antenna ever flown, and three different radar processing techniques, each made by a different radar manufacturer, were used. Two of them, a high-PRF pulse-Doppler by Westinghouse, and a medium-PRF pulse-Doppler by Hughes, were assessed to be worthy of full-scale investigation.

Research contracts were placed with the above two companies and Raytheon in January 1966.

The Overland Radar Technology (ORT) research programme conducted in the late-sixties used a US Air Force EC-121 similar to that illustrated here. The flight-testing permitted the US electronics industry to prove that pulse-Doppler 'look-down' radar capability would be available for an EC-121 replacement

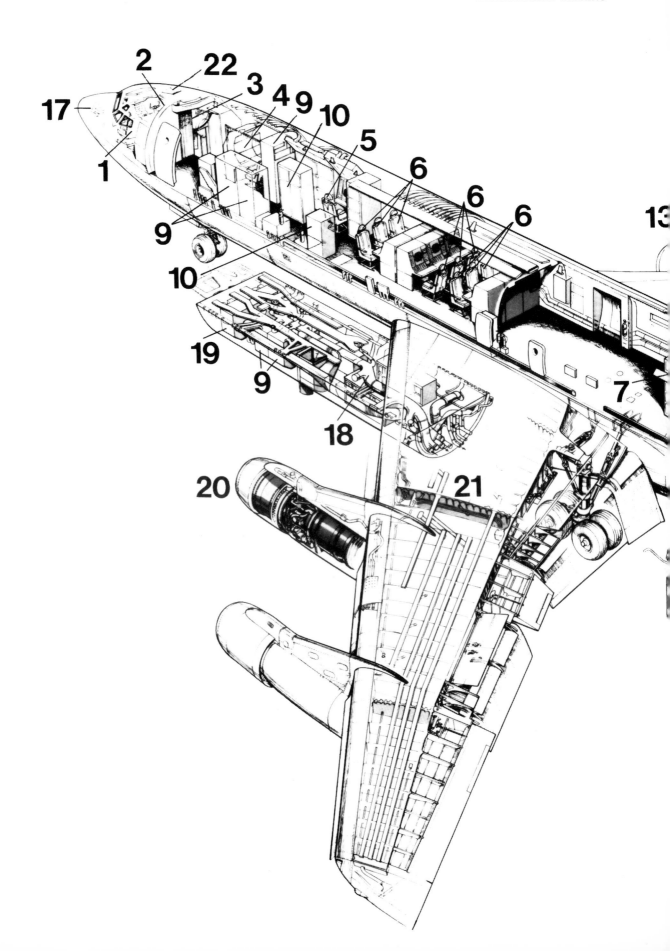

KEY **BOEING E-3A SENTRY**

1 Pilot
2 Co-pilot
3 Navigator
4 Communications operator
5 Computer operator
6 Radar operators
7 Radar maintenance engineer

16 Radar receiver equipment
17 Weather radar
18 Cooling equipment
19 Power supplies
20 Pratt & Whitney TF33-PW-100/100A turbofans each rated at 21,000 lb (93.4 kN) static thrust
21 Fuel tanks—total capacity 73,515 kg (162,024 lb)
22 In-flight refuelling receptacle

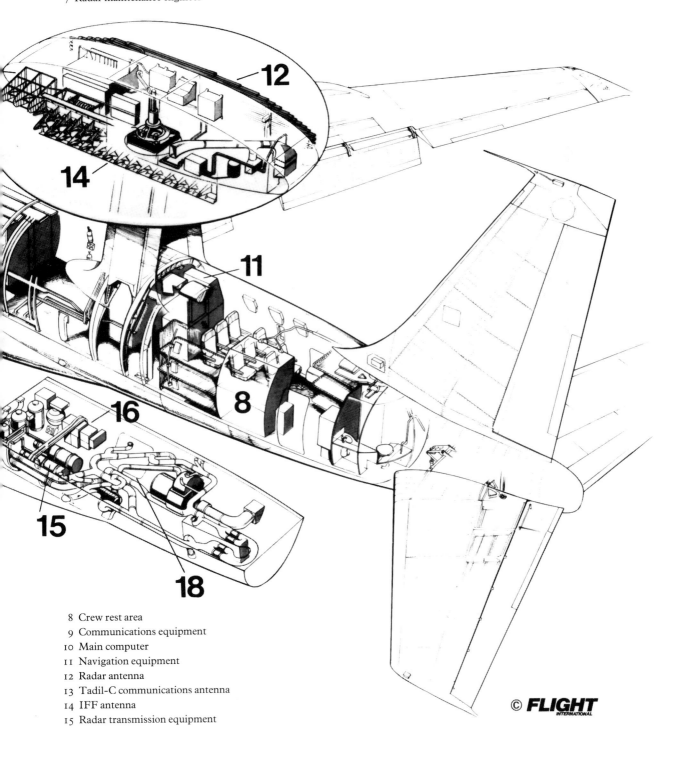

8 Crew rest area
9 Communications equipment
10 Main computer
11 Navigation equipment
12 Radar antenna
13 Tadil-C communications antenna
14 IFF antenna
15 Radar transmission equipment

© *FLIGHT* INTERNATIONAL

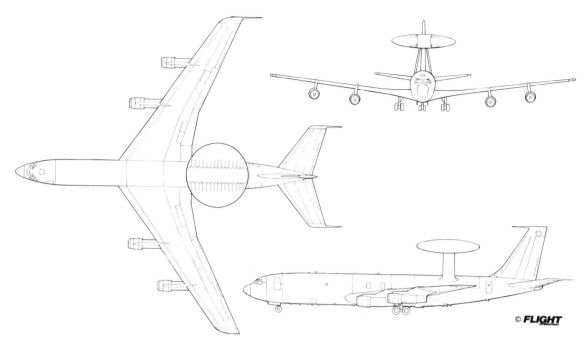

BOEING E-3 SENTRY

Span	44.42 m (145 ft 9 in)
Length	46.61 m (152 ft 11 in)
Max height	12.60 m (41 ft 4 in)
Max gross wt	147,400 kg (325,000 lb)
Max level speed	460 knots

Cruise speed/altitude	400 knots/29,000 ft
Take-off distance	approx 3054 m (10,020 ft)
Patrol performance	6 hours at 870 nm from base

The latter firm was tasked to pit its expertize with large ground-based surveillance radars against the pulse-Doppler systems which the other companies were developing, but it was proved soon afterwards that for an airborne 'look-down' radar the pulse-Doppler submissions, although the most challenging, were certainly the most promising prospects. The US Navy was party to all that was being considered by its colleagues and it kept General Electric (its main AEW radar contractor), aware of pulse-Doppler developments. In August 1967 testing of major radar receiver components was reported by both Westinghouse and Hughes, and contracts were let by the US Air Force for radar-installation feasibility studies.

An operational requirement was issued to the airframe industry, and both Boeing and McDonnell Douglas were funded from 1967 to consider the implications of installing the radar, other sensors, processing and all necessary command and operating crew in a new-generation AEW aircraft. As only a few dozen aircraft were ever likely to be needed, the companies were encouraged to envisage adaption of the existing Boeing 707 and McDonnell Douglas DC-8 airliners. McDonnell Douglas initially considered the long-bodied

DC-8 Series 63, but its definitive proposals used the shorter DC-8 Series 62 aircraft.

In its original guise the air force specification included all the operational attributes of an airborne command post. In addition to acting as an airborne sensor it was to carry senior military personnel and facilities necessary to direct land, sea, or air battles from a mobile command post. This was the origin of the Airborne Warning and Control System (Awacs) acronym, which has tended to stick with the project, and it was a logical extension of the command information centre (CIC) concept practised in the EC-121.

The breadth of what the specification desired was too much, however. McDonnell Douglas could not fit it all into a long-bodied DC-8 and Boeing resorted to consulting the US Air Force on the possibility of using a Boeing 747 with the radar installed in a 12.2 m (40 ft) diameter rotodome. The combined development of a new airframe and a new line of high-by-pass-ratio turbofan engines, neither of which had flown at that time, plus a sophisticated radar and a whole command/control system under one umbrella was overruled. The command post portion of the operational requirement was deleted (and later revived on its own for the Boeing E-4B pro-

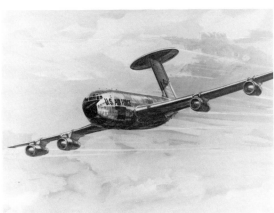

When the US Air Force asked for Airborne Warning and Control System (Awacs) proposals from the US industry, McDonnell Douglas offered a version of the DC-8 Series 62 airliner with a rotodome on four slender pylons

LEFT Boeing engineers initially considered an unusual conversion of the company's 707-320 airliner with a rotodome carried on a swept-forward fin

BELOW Because the initial US Air Force specification called for as much airborne-command capability as possible, Boeing studied an Awacs-version of the company's 747 airliner. This was rejected, although the airborne-command post concept was revived later as the E-4

gramme) and the airborne-warning portion, still with a sizeable proportion of actual control capability, was substituted.

Boeing was awarded the initial Awacs contract, to produce two evaluation aircraft, on 9 July 1970. The company had studied three Boeing 707-320B derivatives, all using rotodome radar installations. The earliest had proposed an airframe with a very broad, swept-forward fin and with the radar mounted on top. Although the radar did not suffer tail-fin blanking in this layout, it was a heavily compromised configuration,

not least because of the large mass carried aft, and
the aerodynamic implications on stability of having the rotodome almost directly above the tailplane. It was superseded by a more-conventional
configuration, which had the rotodome mounted
above the rear fuselage, and the standard 707
empennage.

The airframe companies, who had been asked
to submit designs suitable for long-endurance
missions and including provisions for air-to-air
refuelling, were aware of the benefits which high
by-pass-ratio engines could provide. Boeing
worked on two proposals, one with four Pratt &
Whitney TF-33 engines, which are military derivatives of the airliner's JT-3D powerplants, and
one with eight 9000 lb thrust General Electric
TF-34 turbofans. The latter had two engines
mounted on each pylon, à la Boeing B-52 Stratofortress, and the Air Force assessed it to be the
winning configuration. Initially, however, Boeing was told to proceed with evaluation aircraft
converted from commercial airframes, and with
standard Pratt & Whitney JT-3D engines.

The Boeing submission, in line with any other
large system proposal, had also involved considerable effort by major subcontractors. These
included IBM and Hazeltine Corporation for

computer, and display and control submissions respectively. The two electronic firms have remained an intrinsic part of the Boeing E-3A team throughout its development and operation.

The only big unknown participant in 1970 was the radar manufacturer and the US Air Force Electronic Systems Division was studying proposals submitted by both Westinghouse and Hughes. By now the companies were in a position to deliver brassboard (experimental) radars suitable for airborne trials, and as, on paper, there was little to choose between them—and a lot for both teams to learn from having the chance to dabble in advanced pulse-Doppler technology—both firms were instructed to proceed with the development of flyable hardware. The initial airframe contract to Boeing therefore was to convert two 707-320B airliners, designated EC-137D by the air force, one each to be used to conduct trials with the Hughes and Westinghouse radars.

The first EC-137D flew from Seattle on February 9, 1972, and externally it looked exactly like the Boeing E-3A which was eventually put into production. After the 93-minute first flight Awacs Project Pilot Jim Gannett pronounced that there had been no surprises, and that all test objectives had been met. Aerodynamically, the big rotodome was a non-event. Between 4 April 1972 and 5 September 1972 each of the two evaluation aircraft flew 49 times and accumulated about 290 flying hours, mostly around the Seattle area. In this phase F-4 Phantom, F-106 Delta Dagger and B-52 Stratofortress target aircraft were provided by the US Air Force, and the detection performance of each radar was evaluated over five clutter backgrounds: calm sea, vegetated farmland, rolling woodland, desert and bare mountain peaks. Synthetic targets could be injected at the receiver in both aircraft, and detection performance was evaluated in clear and ECM conditions. It was an exhaustive evaluation from which the US Air Force ESD team declared in October 1972 that Westinghouse was appointed as radar contractor for the programme. The Hughes radar was dismantled and taken back to California, and the experience has since been used to good effect in fighter airborne-

LEFT Announced winner of the US Air Force Awacs competition, in July 1970, was a Boeing submission based on the Boeing 707-320 airliner with eight General Electric TF34 turbofan engines

Boeing converted two airliners into pre-production Awacs airframes, retaining Pratt & Whitney engines. Competing pulse-Doppler radars made by Hughes and Westinghouse were installed and flown in comparative tests during 1972

interception radars, all with 'look down' medium-PRF pulse-Doppler capability. The way that the US Air Force, at relatively modest expense, managed to inject invaluable experience into both radar manufacturers in a very short time, ranks alongside any of the more widely publicized aircraft fly-offs which have kept a keen edge on US technical competitiveness.

On 26 January 1973 a full-scale Awacs development programme was announced. The only surprise was that the Pratt and Whitney TF-33-powered proposal was now pronounced as the basic configuration, and only four pre-production aircraft were to be authorized against an original plan to use six. The type was officially designated Boeing E-3A, and later it was named Sentry. Over the last decade or so however, and especially when politics have brought the purchase of aircraft to the public's attention, the name that has always stuck has been Awacs.

From January 1973, System Integration Development (SID) tasks concentrated solely on the Westinghouse radar, and an Initial Operation Test and Evaluation (IOT&E) programme was to be conducted too. Of the four pre-production aircraft, only two were to be built new. The EC-137D which had carried the Hughes radar was revamped until it was a zero-hour airframe, and the original Westinghouse-equipped EC-137D was later also put through the Boeing factory at Renton with the same objective. They came out indistinguishable from the two new pre-production E-3As which were built. One aircraft was devoted to aerodynamic assessments and did not carry operational avionics, but the other three were well equipped and instrumented. It is the intention that all four aircraft will one day be refurbished and used operationally by the US Air Force.

Production decisions were due to be taken in December 1974, so the SID-IOT&E programme, although it ran from January 1973 to December 1975, was no sleep-walking exercise. Between March 1974 and December 1975 the four aircraft chalked up 294 flights and 1318 flying hours. Considering the complexity and immaturity of the equipment involved, this was an impressive record. Integration with the Norad air-defence system and the inter-operability of US Air Force and US Navy communications systems were amongst the major objectives demon-

Elegant as the E-3 radar installation is, a serious compromise is the amount of downward view blocked by the airframe, and reflections off the fin

strated in this period.

Operationally, rotodome radar installations had proved effective on carrier-borne AEW types where it had been used already, but it does have drawbacks. Not least of these are reflections from the tail-fin in the rear sector of the radar coverage, and an appreciable degree of close-range blanking due to the airframe. On the Boeing E-3A the rotodome is further aft than the radar designer might have preferred, causing the wings and forward fuselage to block a lot of downward view ahead and abeam the aircraft. In level flight shadowing does not affect the important areas beyond about 25 nm from the aircraft, when operating at 29,000 ft altitude, but at a typical flight incidence of 4° the nose can blank the view forward as far as 40 nm. US engineers have always applauded the simplicity of rotodome installations compared to alternatives such as fore-and-aft scanners, but the compromise is all too clear when blanking effects are taken into account.

By keeping the radome well aft of the aircraft centre-of-gravity positive directional stability was assured, but to balance the aircraft most of the on-board equipment, with the exception of the radar, is mounted in the forward fuselage.

The Westinghouse AN/APY-2 radar uses a mixture of phased-array and slotted-waveguide technology. A great attribute is that in a banked turn such as this, the radar beam is stabilized in space by the electronic phase shifters

Aerodynamic interference has been minimised by adopting two inward-sloping pylons which are not directly ahead of the fin, and an advantage of this configuration welcomed by radar engineers was the opportunity to segregate transmitter and receiver waveguides to port and starboard respectively.

In the rotodome there are two independent antenna installations, arranged back-to-back. These are the radar and IFF with TADIL-C arrays. The radar antenna comprises 30 vertically-stacked slotted-waveguide sticks and it measures 7.3 m (24 ft) across and 1.5 m (5 ft) deep. This produces an efficient radiation pattern. It manages to emit almost all of its energy in an approximately one-degree wide beam with relatively small sidelobes. Reception, using the same antenna, is also highly directional. As the aircraft cruises, the rotodome rotates at 6 rpm to provide 360° azimuth coverage. Phased-array technology is also incorporated in the antenna in the shape of phase-shifters behind the antenna apertures.

Boeing E-3A flight-deck, except for such military standards as four-man seating arrangement and vertical-tape engine instrumentation, is close to airliner configuration

When the aircraft banks in a turn the phase-shifters deflect the beam vertically to stabilize the radar relative to the earth. Surveillance is continuous therefore without having to resort to skidding around an unco-ordinated turn, as is the case with the E-2 Hawkeye system. Vertical beam scanning in level flight can also provide height-finding capability.

The IFF array is smaller than the radar antenna, and is an arrangement of small groups of aerials and feeders which can interrogate and receive data in a small azimuth angle. Data which it receives, although 180°-opposed to the radar, can be correlated with radar plots to provide positive identification of friendly tracks. The IFF antenna is flanked by small TADIL-C data-link arrays whose function is solely to communicate with other friendly aircraft.

Structurally the rotodome centre-section is an oval box, 9 m (30 ft) across, 1.8 m (6 ft) high and 1.8 m (6 ft) deep, which supports the antennas on each oval face. To streamline it, black radar-transparent radomes, almost semi-circular in planform are added to each side. These are by no means simple, their shape and thickness having to satisfy streamlining requirements, to transmit radar energy undistorted, and to meet demanding airload requirements. The latter can amount to a static pitching moment of up to 30,000 kg-m (2 million lb-in). When the radar is not operational the rotodome rotates at a lazy $\frac{1}{4}$ rpm to maintain an even distribution of lubricants on bearing surfaces.

The Westinghouse AN/APY-2 radar (AN/APY-1 on the first 21 USAF aircraft, but all are being up-graded to the newer radar standard) equipment is housed in the rear fuselage. The S-band (2–4 GHz) transmitter is in the lower port section and is rated at 8 KW mean power output (400 KW peak power output). About half of the hold space beneath the cabin floor is taken up by eight pressurized containers enclosing a klystron/pulser unit, which generates the radar pulses, a travelling-wave tube driver unit, and high-voltage transformers and filter units. As much as possible in the transmitter system uses solid-state

The communications officer has access to a great variety of
radio-communication systems. He can patch the aircraft
into local VHF nets, or global HF radio systems, and has
an ever expanding selection of secure transmission systems
at his disposal

components, to assure reliability. The klystron
pulse-generator and TWT-driver contain the
only tube in the system. A redundant transmitter
design provides some degree of component failure–survival, and in the event of a unit needing
to be replaced in flight there is an overhead rail
in the bay which permits new equipment to be
lowered in by the radar-maintenance engineer.

Most of the remaining bay volume is occupied
with electro-magnetic interference filters, notch
filters and drive units, and electronic decoders.
All the radar equipment is cooled by a heat-
exchanger and forced-air cooling system. A
liquid-cooling system from the klystron radiates
heat out through the belly skin between the wing-
roots, while cooling air is taken in, during flight,
through a small ram-air scoop above and aft of
the port wing root. A small bank of fans ensures
that adequate air circulation is available during

All electronic operations on an E-3 are connected in some
way to the IBM computer which this operator monitors.
The illuminated 'BOOBE' is a computer start-up command

ground-running, when the radar system may be on stand-by and dissipating considerable heat.

Much of the receiver processing is conducted in equipment installed in the aircraft cabin. This is immediately above the filter banks in the underfloor bay, and includes all software-controlled equipment so that computer program maintenance can be carried out conveniently, even during flight.

So far attention has concentrated on the radar and its associated equipment, with a mention of IFF and TADIL-C but the large number of sensors necessary on an AEW aircraft means that many more, less obtrusive, aerials must festoon the airframe. Some are similar to conventional airliner sensors, like the VOR/localiser antenna embedded in the tail fin, and ADF loop and sense and VHF radio blade antennas on the fuselage

keel. There are plenty of extras. HF radio antennas point aft from the starboard wing tip, and forward from the fin tip, and an HF radio notch antenna is embedded in the aft portion of the fin tip. Also in the fin tip is provision for small spiral antennas which in conjunction with similar units at each tailplane tip—and possibly one more in the nose, which remains unacknowledged—will comprise the passive detection system (PDS). This was not installed in US Air Force E-3As, as Continental-US protection was assessed to be adequate using radar and IFF only. It may have been added subsequently, as it would make sense in aircraft deployed to many sensitive parts of the world, and in Nato aircraft, but it is the sort of decision that would be taken as quietly as possible. Some rumours suggest that the option has been taken up already in the US-enhancement

The nine radar operators in an E-3 sit in three rows, and each has an identical workstation with ITT displays

BELOW In the rear fuselage, and just below the radome, a radar maintenance engineer has a workstation where he can probe into radar equipment and program operations

BOTTOM The main computer provides synthetic display data, such as coastline and danger area outlines, as well as aircraft identity labels and data tables

programme, which is described later. Last but by no means least important of the antennas on an E-3A are the many units along the keel. These provide comprehensive VHF and UHF radio communications, and there are radio altimeter, Doppler-navigation radar, Tacan and marker beacon sensors.

Many of the aerials are linked to equipment in what was the forward baggage bay of the original airliner. In this area there are several communication equipment racks, and the whole of the aircraft electrical power-distribution system. There is also a cut out in the forward keel area and a chute from the cabin which permits the crew to bail out in an emergency. The forward bay, like the rear underfloor bay, is riddled with cooling-air supplies and cable ducts. Most of the cabin air supply for the radar operators and their

Looking curiously incomplete an E-3 rolls off the assembly line with neither paint scheme nor rotodome

Boeing's Renton factory has built all E-3s, alongside Boeing 727 and 737 airliners

equipment is fed into the cabin through risers in the aft portion of the forward underfloor bay.

The floor area of an E-3A holds plenty of interest to anyone walking through the aircraft. From the front, one starts with a very airliner-style flight-deck, accommodating pilot, co-pilot and navigator. Provision for up to two further crewmen is available. The aircrew has a toilet adjacent to the flight deck. Opposite is the forward entrance, which is used by all the crew during normal turnrounds. Moving aft in the cabin one passes the communications console (on the left when walking aft), communication racks left and right, the central data-exchange area and main computer (all to the left) and then one has to move right to walk by three lines of display consoles. Each line accommodates three operators, the first row facing aft, the next row facing forward, and the final trio again facing aft. Behind them is an empty area where the airborne commander and his staff would have had to fit, had the spirit of the original specification been maintained. Although clearly not a design objective, the space has been used on more than one oc-

casion as an impromptu cinema and briefing area for three dozen or so guests when aircraft have gone on tour. It is impressive to be briefed on-board rather than merely walked around after a bewildering exposure to slides and chat in an air-side cinema.

Still moving aft, and now slightly ahead of the rotodome supports, the radar-maintenance station appears facing aft on the left. Behind this the rotodome supports are inconspicious, except for a slight thickening of the walls where deep frames carry the support pylon loads into the fuselage structure, and behind these are the navigation and IFF equipment racks. It comes as a surprise to find that there is still room to accommodate three bunks and a galley on the port side, with three rows of aft-facing seats for eight crewmen on the starboard side, followed by the rear entrance, facing three more bunks, a sizeable survival equipment locker and, last of all, a toilet and washroom.

Significant differences from the original airliner, which are visible externally, in addition to the obvious rotodome, are an in-flight refuelling probe receptacle in the forward fuselage roof, almost above the cockpit, and four military rated Pratt & Whitney TF33-P-7/7A turbofans each rated at 21,500 lb (95.6 kN) static thrust at sea level, on the underwing pylons. Each engine has two 75 kVA generators providing up to 600 kVA total power.

The radar, IFF and (when the provision is taken up) the passive detection system all feed data to an IBM central computer in the forward cabin area. Since early 1981 all production aircraft have used a CC-2 standard computer. This has replaced the older CC-1 units, which was based on the commercially-available IBM 4 Pi model, and it is being retrofitted to early production aircraft. From its 6.5 kW power supply CC-2 can complete two million instructions every second (CC-1 handled 740,000 per second) and has access to 2.5 million bits of information. The whole system occupies a cabinet about the size of a small wardrobe. Its thousands of words of computer program represent a tremendous investment in terms of manpower and development effort. The airborne operational computer program (AOCP) conducts target tracking and identification functions, co-ordinates communications between the aircraft and other points in the air-defence network, records, analyses and displays data, and can be used for on-board operator training. Extra programs can be loaded, in-flight or on the ground, to conduct system exercises and analyse the results, to operate training positions and to complete ground-support and computer-program maintenance tasks.

Track files for up to 100 targets could be accommodated in random-access memory initially, and these were monitored continuously by the CC-1 unit. Soon after service introduction with the US Air Force the track file capacity was increased to 200 targets. With the introduction of the CC-2 processor, up to 400 simultaneous track files can be maintained. It was Nato's requirement to track dense traffic over Western Europe, plus US Air Force desires that prompted the substitution of the more capable processor. Automatic track identification and initiation were not available initially but these have been outstanding objectives which should be incorporated as software development progresses. Indeed, in its earliest form, with a track capacity of 100 only, no auto-track initiation and nine operators, the aircraft was rudimentary compared to what could have been expected. E-3A central computer development has been introducing new capability at a regular rate however, reflecting the efficiency of a remarkably well thought-out systems-management programme which has supported the basic airframe and sensor technology development programmes. The total development effort has kept a large team of scientists and engineers employed in various companies spread across the US, and lately in West Germany too. Their efforts ensure that E-3 capability isn't likely to reach a plateau for a long time yet.

The nine radar operators face identical Hazeltine-developed consoles. The display in the

BELOW A brand-new E-3, the first of 18 destined to join NATO, concludes its maiden flight at Boeing Field

RIGHT The last major assembly item, the rotodome, is added at Boeing Field, and following this an intensive equipment installation plan swings into action. Forlorn YC-14 in background

centre of each unit is a rectangular green-phosphor cathode-ray tube on which the operator can select either graphic or tabular data formats. Banks of switches to left and right are used to sift out various target and background data categories, to control communication channels and to select radar surveillance functions. On his desk, each controller has a trackball, which when rolled by the fingers moves a cursor mark on his display. There is also an alphanumeric keyboard and various alarm/display control selectors.

Target data on the displays can be derived from any of the aircraft sensors, and where sensor performance needs to be modified to meet particular situations the operators have some control over the detection techniques used. The radar, for example, can be switched to either passive or active operation in any one of 32 sectors. The

most frequently used active mode, overland, are the pulse-Doppler non-elevation scan (PDNES) which operates the radar in its basic surveillance mode, or pulse-Doppler elevation scan (PDES) mode, which uses the antenna-mounted phase-shifters to scan the radar beam vertically as pulses are emitted, and so can provide an indication of target elevation. Beyond-the-horizon (BTH) mode is a non-Doppler operation which provides target bearing and range data at ranges where the horizon begins to mask low-level targets. Since operations began with Nato-operated E-3As a maritime-surveillance mode has become available too.

Communication link operations are numerous

Painted, and with all systems intact, except for the most confidential of on-board software, a brand-new Boeing E-3 merges onto the apron at Boeing Field

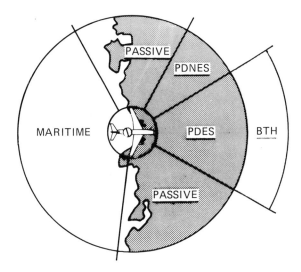

Typical radar mode utilisation
This Boeing released impression shows typical radar mode
utilisations and illustrates well how an AEW commander
can regulate radar operation, even in a single-scan, to get
the best out of his system. The modes shown are:

MARITIME   – low-PRF to see surface targets
PASSIVE   – radar switched off over regions where
              surveillance is not required
PDNES   – pulse-Doppler, no elevation scan: target
              range and bearing data only
PDES   – pulse-Doppler, elevation scan: target
              range, bearing and height data
BTH   – beyond-the-horizon: special mode to see
              high-flying targets beyond the cut-off range
              for low-flying targets

and can use many radio devices that are best
listed with their major uses. The principles used
are straight-forward. UHF and VHF links are
used for line-of-sight communications, and HF
radio primarily for beyond line-of-sight links.
The combination of narrow-band, wide-band,
secure voice or clear voice facilities illustrates the
degree to which data in and out of an AEW aircraft has to be protected. TADIL-C deserves a
special mention because its highly-directional
antenna has already been described in the rotodome. It is a directional link, and therefore very
difficult to jam.

E-3As were amongst the first types to have a
new communication system, originally known as
Time Division Multiple Access (TDMA) but
now officially called Joint Tactical Information
Distribution System (Jtids). This is a modular
system, still being developed by the US and Nato
nations, and it will be a very comprehensive data-
link system when it is fully operational. It passes
messages in patterned sequences, the smallest
message element being a 7.8125 millisecond
'timeslot'. During any 12-second period, called
a 'cycle', some 1536 timeslots are available, and
successive cycles of operations will link AEW air-

craft with other AEW aircraft, ground network
stations, ships, other aircraft and so on. In-
frequent users can butt into the datalink at intervals designated in up to 64 cycles, making a 12.8
min response the minimum utilisation possible.
This period is called the 'epoch' in Jtids pattern
terminology. The full system will be used to link
Nato-operated E-3As and British AEW Nimrods
in joint operations over Europe in the late-1980s,
and will be introduced into US Air Force aircraft
concurrently.

Other functions include navigation and guidance control, using several on-board sensors.
Two Delco ASN-119 Carousel IV inertial navigation sets are installed, plus a Northrop ARN-
120 receiver and a Ryan APN-213 Doppler radar
navigator. The automatic correlation of the data
from this comprehensive mix of dead-reckoning

Boeing E-3 Sentry communication links

Function	Type	Application
E-3 to E-3	UHF high power (full duplex)	NBSV, CV, TADIL-A
E-3 to mission aircraft	UHF high power	TADIL-C
E-3 to mission aircraft	UHF medium power (simplex)	WBSV, CV
E-3 to mission aircraft	VHF-AM (simplex)	CV
E-3 to ground	UHF medium power (duplex or simplex)	WBSV, CV, TADIL-A
E-3 to ground	VHF-FM (simplex)	CV
E-3 to ground	VHF-AM (simplex)	CV
E-3 to ground or airborne	HF SSB (duplex or simplex)	NBSV, CV
E-3 to ground or airborne	HF SSB (net operations)	TADIL-A
Emergency	UHF Guard UHF ADF	CV Audio
	VHF-AM Guard	CV
Flight deck	UHF medium power (simplex)	CV

AM = amplitude modulation
FM = frequency modulation
SSB = single sideband
NBSV = narrow-band secure voice
CV = clear voice
WBSV = wide-band secure voice
VHF = verh high frequency
UHF = ultra high frequency
HF = high frequency

and radio navaid sets assures the crew of highly-accurate position data at all time, and is vital too to the orientation and stabilisation of display data. As a check on the system, the radar display will soon show up any significant position slippage, and additional navigation inputs can be obtained by relative-navigation facilities provided by the Jtids communication system. Flight path data can be fed directly to the E-3A autopilot for automatic patrol-pattern flying.

Initial flying by the two converted Boeing 707-320Bs was called Phase 1A Brassboard development. It demonstrated E-3 system feasibility, completed the evaluation necessary to select one of the competing radars and it showed that the proposed system could acquire and track a number of targets simultaneously. A small amount of System Integration Development (SID) work was involved in the latter days of flying the two first aircraft, and this became a preoccupation in the four-aircraft Phase 1B full-scale development programme. This was started in January 1973 and eventually completed in May 1977, by which time the fleet of aircraft had accumulated 4573 flying hours and 986 flights.

US Air Force production E-3As had been authorized in April 1975, although long-lead item procurement had gone ahead as early as January 1974. The initial production order led the way for 22 aircraft to be delivered to the US Air Force, at Tinker AFB, Oklahoma, between March 1977 and March 1981. These were US 'Core' standard aircraft which included the IBM CC-1 central computer and a AN/APY-1 radar, whose overwater target detection capability was limited to calm sea conditions only.

Development of the 'enhanced' USAF model was started in September 1974. Although casual observers cannot tell the difference between this and an earlier model it is a vastly more capable aircraft, as it includes the AN/APY-2 radar and CC-2 central computer, plus several other systems improvements. All production E-3As, starting with the 23rd aircraft for the US Air Force, which came off the Renton production line in December 1981, have been to this standard and are now designated E-3C. The 31st, and currently the last US Air Force delivery (excluding the four refurbished pre-production aircraft) should take place in May 1984. Between writing and publication the US Air Force E-3 order seems sure to be extended by 12 aircraft however.

In early 1978 Boeing had almost a year's production at the factory, following a spate of industrial action. It provided an opportunity to capture a rare view of five E-3s in pristine condition, and ready for service

Photographed shortly after take-off, this US Air Force E-3 shows that not all AEW types are downright ugly. Most of the 707-airliner elegance has survived

LEFT US Air Force rapid deployment operations have shown the wisdom of having in-flight refuelling capability. This E-3 takes on fuel from a generic ancestor, a Boeing KC-135 Stratotanker

RIGHT Stratotanker boom-operator's view of an E-3 closing in for a fill-up

Boeing E-3 Sentry title (Awacs was the specification name which the press has curiously remembered) alludes to day and night operations along sensitive coasts and borders throughout the world

Work is already in hand too to upgrade the first 22 production aircraft to US 'enhanced' standard, and they will be reclassified as E-3B aircraft.

Senior Nato ministers approved the acquisition of 18 E-3As in December 1978, after a long and bitter political struggle in Europe, the tale of which is told elsewhere in these pages. This was the first overseas contract for the type (ignoring an intention to buy which was later cancelled by Iran), and Boeing had started work against Nato requirements as early as January 1973. Official go-ahead was given to the manufacturers by the US Government in January 1979 and the first Nato E-3A was handed over at Seattle on January 17, 1981. It was delivered exactly two months later to Dornier at Oberpfaffenhofen in West Germany where avionics were installed as part of the offset deal with Nato countries. Dornier plans to deliver the 18th and final E-3A to Nato in June 1985.

Five examples of the Boeing E-3A Sentry have also been requested by Saudi Arabia, again stimulating a heady political fight, this time in the US Congress. They are due to be delivered by the end of 1985, and excluding four refurbishments for the US Air Force that will take total E-3A production to 54 aircraft over 9 years. As hinted above, US Air Force production for 12 more aircraft is almost certain to be authorized, and there are several other sales possibilities. Egypt, a doubtful but often mentioned potential E-3A operator was confirmed as an E-2 customer as this book went to press, and France is a nation that the US will certainly accommodate as an E-3 customer if politics and price can be matched.

Finally, the vexed question of costs. Boeing claims that total E-3 development, including all related ORT programme work and the various stages of the aircraft development programme, amounted by 1982 to a $1500 million investment. A more definitive figure cannot be prised out. The 1983 Fiscal Year request by the US Air Force was for just two aircraft, and it totalled $315.6 m; but don't jump the gun as many have done. This is split into $166.3 m for new aircraft (suggesting a price tag of $83.15 m each). $80.4 m for spares and support in respect of more than two dozen aircraft in service (or about $3 m per year each) and $78.9 m for research, development, test and evaluation work still in progress. A personal view of the latter is that it indicates a team of perhaps 1500 people still employed on E-3 development. That means that although this chapter brings the E-3 Sentry programme up-to-date, it isn't the end of the story.

KEY **BRITISH AEROSPACE NIMROD AEW.3**

1 Pilot
2 Co-pilot
3 Navigator
4 Communications operator
5 Radar operators
6 Crew rest area and toilet
7 Communications equipment
8 Radar transmitter equipment
9 IFF equipment
10 Main computer
11 Radar receiver equipment

12 Cooling equipment
13 Power supplies
14 ESM antenna
15 Radar antenna
16 IFF antenna (embodied in radar antenna)
17 Weather radar
18 ESM cabinet
19 Mission recorder
20 Powerplants—four Rolls-Royce RB.168-20 Spey
   Mk. 250 turbofans, each rated at 12,140 lb (54 kN) static
   thrust.
21 Fuel tanks—standard capacity 38,940 kg (85,840 lb)

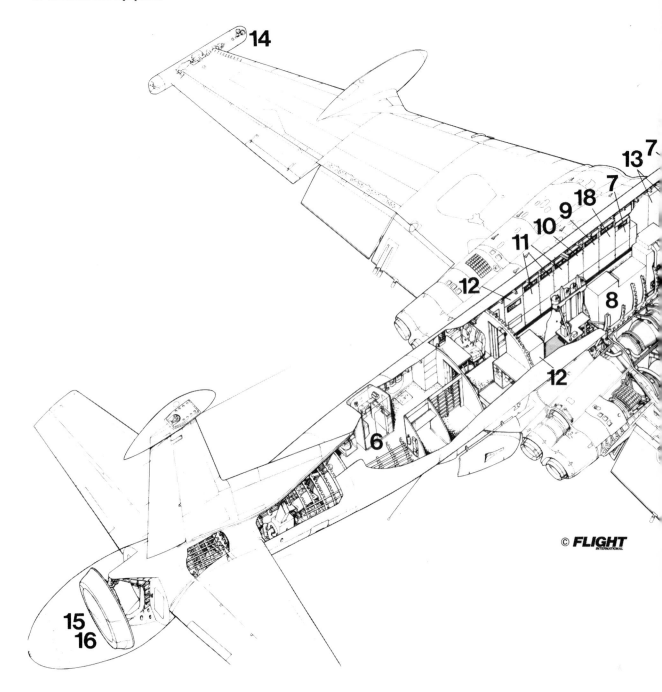

Chapter 9
British Aerospace Nimrod AEW.3

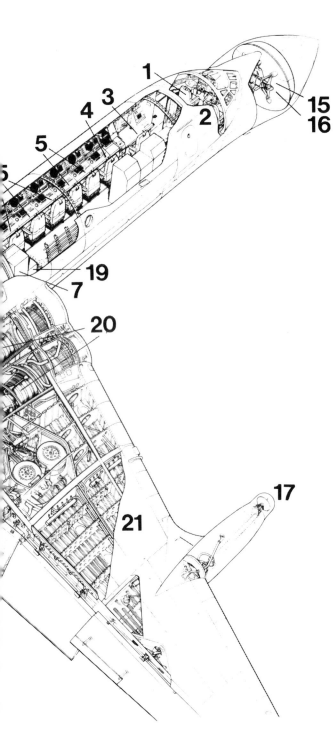

The genesis of Britain's leading AEW programme, and until the lessons of the Falkland Islands crisis in 1982, its only current AEW programme, is charted in detail at Chapter 6. The elements of what went on in the ten years or so before the 'Shackleton-replacement' programme was formally launched in 1972 deserve a brief recap.

Britain decided, around 1963, that its fleet of Gannet AEW aircraft would need replacement. The Admiralty was the sole source of funding initially, and its requirements especially called for carrier-based AEW. The decision was taken by scientists and engineers to develop a frequency-modulated intermittent continuous wave (FMICW) radar, using two similar radar antennas, each scanning a 180° wide sector, mounted fore and aft on an airframe. These were to be inverted-cassegrain type aerials, and their locations eliminated radar-blanking problems.

When carrier requirements were abandoned, after swingeing defence cuts in 1965, there was at last interest in land-based AEW types, and several proposals were put forward. Amongst these, in August 1966, was a plan to adapt the HS.801 anti-submarine warfare aircraft, which was then in development. It is now in service with the RAF as the BAe Nimrod MR.2 (all MR.1 examples having been updated). Circular fore and aft scanners were proposed.

The Treasury judged the project to be too expensive and, in effect, told the MoD to tell industry how to do its job. Against all commonsense the same specification was used to guide the design of an HS.748 Andover military-freighter derivative, As expected, it turned out to be too small to perform adequately. The AEW Nimrod proposal remained the front-runner and was used as a reference for development work which, starting in 1968, saw a Comet airframe adapted to carry the nose radar installation proposed for the definitive aircraft. It now used a 2.44×1.83 m (8×6 ft) elliptical scanner. In 1971 technology threatened to overtake the project and all work has halted while the nation's scien-

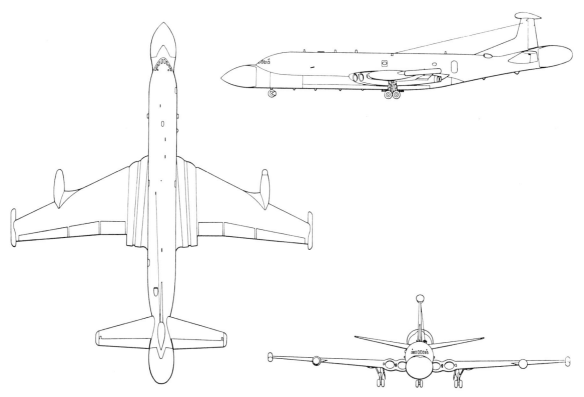

BRITISH AEROSPACE AEW NIMROD

Span	35.08 m (115 ft 1 in)
Length	41.97 m (137 ft 8 in)
Max height	10.67 m (35 ft 0 in)
Max gross wt	80,510 kg (177,500 lb)

Max level speed	500 knots
Cruise speed/altitude	400 knots/30,000 ft
Take-off distance	1463 m (5300 ft)
Patrol performance	approx 7 hours at 700 nm from base

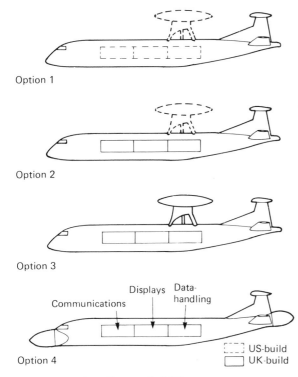

Option 1

Option 2

Option 3

Communications   Displays   Data-handling

Option 4

US-build
UK-build

AEW Nimrod studies: early 1970s
Project-definition studies for the AEW Nimrod
concentrated on four major options which had various
combinations of US and UK-build of the Grumman E-2
Hawkeye system, or an all-new fore-and-aft scanner
system (FASS) which was largely similar to the original
1966 AEW Nimrod proposal described in Chapter 6

tists grappled with the pros and cons of FMICW
versus pulse-Doppler radar. The debate has been
reported fully in Chapter 6, and the facts that led
to the debate coming down, eventually, in favour
of pulse-Doppler radar processing. It was from
this point, around 1972, that the actual AEW
Nimrod programme can be traced without
interruption.

Official funding for a Shackleton replacement
was released in 1972. With most Shackletons
already between 15–20 years old there was some
pressure to get on with the job quickly, and not
least because the Boeing E-3A was about to enter
flight-test in America. The project proceeded
formally and ponderously. In the first instance
the chosen subcontractors, Hawker Siddeley
Aviation at Manchester and Marconi-Elliott
(formerly Elliott Brothers) at Borehamwood, had
to complete project feasibility studies. They
surveyed existing AEW technology and were
instructed to assess configurations based on the
basic Nimrod airframe. Four different designs
were considered in detail.

Option 1 was a Nimrod airframe with the complete radar and avionics system used in the
Grumman E-2C Hawkeye. At this time the UK
was privy to the capabilities of the AN/APS-125
radar which was under trial in the US, and was
well aware of how soon it could have an operable
AEW system if it used the American equipment.

Option 2 tried to capitalize on the timescale advantage of using the US radar, but integrated it
with all-British data-handling, displays and communication systems. This was much more likely
to provide benefits to the UK industries who had
invested in the appropriate technologies.

Option 3 carried the above concept a stage
further. The US was to supply the AN/APA-171
radome and antenna only, and the radar transmitter and receiver would be made in the UK.
An all-British associated avionics were used too.
This seems to have been the least likely of all the
options, but it was a useful baseline design for
many of the technical and financial assessments.

Option 4 resurrected the original AEW Nimrod proposal made in 1966. It used an all-British
radar and mission avionics systems, albeit that
several items would have to be licence-built US
products, and was the only option to have a fore
and aft scanner system. The switch to pulse-
Doppler processing was taken into account, and
this was also the only proposal to consider an S-

British Aerospace Nimrod MR.2P armed with Sidewinder
AAMs. The Nimrod is a derivative of the Comet airliner

band (2 to 4 GHz frequency) radar. Technically, this was the option that was most likely to make sense. On the other hand it was also the one involving most technical risk, and it was liable to be the most expensive of the possibilities.

Nevertheless, at the end of 1974 Option 4 was assessed to be the most suitable project. Unofficial comments have made it clear that by now the Treasury was well aware of the seriousness of Britain's natural AEW requirements, and was willing to concede that the extra cost of tailoring the job exactly to UK desires, and with full national control of all technical aspects was well worth the extra cost involved. Britain had invested substantially already, albeit in a rather piecemeal fashion and a strongly held view was that Britain had nothing to lose by going it alone. To participate in a Nato purchase of the Boeing E-3A would be just as expensive.

Politicians, at first, argued that Britain was obliged to combine its AEW requirements with those of Nato allies in Western Europe, although no attempt was to be made to convince Europe that it ought to join in the AEW Nimrod programme. Nato had already evaluated the Boeing E-3A, which the US Government had been funding since early 1973 as a Nato-potential system (the funding was to add overwater capability to what was an essentially overland low-flying aircraft detection system). Indeed, in April 1974 a pre-production E-3A was in Europe for three weeks to give demonstrations to high-ranking officials. Everyone in Nato apparently wanted to do part of the job in a work-sharing scheme, and the American proposals could not be matched by anything that Britain could offer.

After all the project feasibility work, the MoD decided that despite no positive interest from Europe it must continue to fund UK AEW work through the project definition stages. It gave the nation something to fall back on if Nato proposals did not materialize. Keeping AEW Nimrod ticking over was costing as much as £1 million per month in early 1977 however, and with no signs yet of a go-ahead decision in Europe, Britain became very restless. Hints were dropped that the UK would go it alone with a national AEW programme if Nato continued to vacillate, and to prove their seriousness the Comet trials aircraft was already being prepared again.

Britain's Defence Secretary Fred Mulley, although notorious at the time for having exhi-

AEW Nimrod hardware first flew in this converted Comet airliner, which conducted radar trials between 1977 and 1982 with a complete radar system, except for the aft antenna

A view of the Comet interior showing typical display and instrumentation equipment. Test electronics were housed on racks beneath the consoles

bited a propensity to fall asleep at air displays, was reported to have negotiated toughly in sessions of the Nato defence planning committee. The full story of the row that broke out, in part based on purile assumptions, but also with its serious side too, is disclosed in Chapter 12.

What is important is to note that on 1 March 1977 the Comet was structurally complete and was rolled-out at Woodford with the sort of ceremony that hardly befitted such an unrepresentative aircraft. This was clearly deliberate, as the next Nato defence planning committee meeting to discuss AEW procurement was a little over three weeks away. On 25 March the Nato men met, they mumbled, they adjourned. Six days later Fred Mulley gave the green light to Hawker Siddeley (soon to be merged with British Aircraft Corporation to form British Aerospace) and Marconi-Elliott (soon to be renamed Marconi Avionics) as airframe and mission-avionics system subcontractors respectively for a £300 million programme to build and deliver 11 examples of Nimrod AEW.3.

One reason why Britain always displayed some reticence about operating the Boeing E-3A, or Grumman E-2C, was that her operational requirement was, and still is, the most ambitious in the world. The radar specification calls for uninterrupted oversea view of vessels and low-flying aircraft, with detection capabilities which equal or exceed the best demonstrated at the time the requirement was prepared, and radar performance has to suffer the minimum of degradation when looking for low-flying targets overland. The aircraft needs to have as comprehensive a radar, IFF and passive-detection system as the E-2C, although the British call the latter an electronic support measure (ESM) system. A vast central computer capability was obviously required, and the specification insisted, from the very beginning, that it should have the ability to automatically initiate and track up to 400 targets simultaneously. Up to six operator's stations were specified, including communications control, and this was considerably less than the E-3A which conducts a similar role. If the Nimrod was used however, it would be difficult to fit more people into the crowded cabin, and this was also the reason for insisting that auto-track initiation was included in the basic system. Not widely

publicized, but typical of the thoroughness that the specification writers could muster after almost 20 years of drafting requirements, were such details as the maximum time it would take for any information to reach the operator after a request. It is a few seconds only, and at the time it was written it was faster than any other system could demonstrate.

Although Britain has gone alone, there has never been any question of her attempting to steer a single-handed path in the European AEW scene. At all times since it was launched as a UK-only venture AEW Nimrod has been credited with a comprehensive communication system,

based on the Jtids-concept, which will permit co-ordinated operations with Nato-operated Boeing E-3As. This has been important since, after Britain had pulled out of the combined programme, Nato did eventually choose the Boeing aircraft. Britain's 11 Nimrod AEW.3s have to operate alongside 18 Nato-owned Boeing E-3As from 1985.

Avid aircraft enthusiasts will know of Nimrod's antecedence from the Comet airliner. The Comet 4 airframe was modified for the basic Nimrod by fitting four Rolls-Royce RB.168 Spey Mk.250 turbofan engines (replacing Avon turbojets) and a bulbous pannier which provides stor-

age volume beneath the basic pressure shell. The anti-submarine versions of Nimrod carry torpedoes and other bulky weapons in this streamlined cavity, and to maintain directional stability, especially when the bomb-bay doors are open, a larger fin with a dorsal extension is used. The basic Nimrod has a deep nose which looks like a skull from the front—it is called the prow by some maritime types. It is this part of the aircraft, far from lovely compared to the original Comet, that for AEW Nimrod is disfigured further by the addition of the forward radar installation. It is clumsy-looking, much wider than the fuselage on which it is attached, and complemented by the

The first AEW Nimrod was an aerodynamic prototype, later fitted with a full internal suite of systems. It revealed for the first time the true ugliness of Britain's highly practical fore-and-aft scanner arrangement, and the wing-tip pods which house passive electronic sensors

equally curious-looking tail radome. Externally, with a few other details that need closer scrutiny to find, these fuselage appendages are the hallmarks of the Nimrod AEW.3.

AEW Nimrod is a little over half the mass of the Boeing E-3, yet about three times the mass of the Grumman E-2C. Consequently nothing is so tightly packed as on the E-2C, but there is none of the spare volume that can be found on the E-3. Six operator's position (four for radar, one for communications and one for ESM systems) and a navigator, plus a few spare crewmen on a typical 10 hours mission, replace some 100 seats in the basic airliner. But they are not spread about in an opulent fashion. They sit in a line when on duty, facing the port wall of the cabin, and apart from the crew rest area the remainder of the cabin floor is taken up with cabinets of electronics which hum and hiss with the energy of their electrical and cooling-air supplies. Before taking a detailed look at the cabin a few observations of the radar antenna system, and some of the implications of its unusual features are in order.

The Marconi-developed radar has two 2.42 × 1.83 m (8 × 6 ft) elliptical antennas. They are identical inverted-cassegrain units with hyperboloid sub-dishes. Each antenna is cantilevered on a two-point suspension so that it can be scanned through 180° in azimuth, and a second, horizontally-aligned pivot, provides roll-stabilization during turns.

As the antennas do not use phase-shifters they have a constant radiation pattern, irrespective of the relative position of targets and aircraft attitude. Each radome is a single moulded unit. The fore and aft installations have slightly different profiles because the forward unit had to be pointed at the nose to meet aerodynamic and birdstrike requirements, while a bluff rear radome gave more predictable airflow breakaway round the aft section of the fuselage.

Contrary to the traditional manners of his profession the Nimrod aerodynamicist accepted a lot of rearward-facing structure just aft of the radome. Compromise is the art of design, and the designer has compromised aerodynamic shape for the necessary radar field-of-view, and to match the radome with a fuselage that is considerably narrower. Flow breakaway is inevitable, and many hours of wind tunnel tests were devoted to investigations into the effects of airflow into the engines, which are buried in the wing-roots, and are barely 9 m (30 ft) aft of the re-entrant section. The aft antenna is at the extre-

mity of a new section of rear fuselage, and is mounted high to retain rotation clearance on take-off. From aft of the circular rear pressure bulkhead the fuselage sweeps up more than on a standard Nimrod, at first tapering inwards then, in planform, gradually expanding to the radome bulkhead section, which is a horizontal ellipse. Almost unnoticeable is a slight increase in tailplane and elevator span. The basic Nimrod fin and tip pod is retained, the latter enclosing electronic sensors about which little is ever uttered.

If one steps inside a Nimrod cabin during production, the scene before equipment is installed is very similar to that in the original Comet, except that it has a lot more wiring bunched along the frames and beneath the floor, and cooling-air ducts seem to be everywhere. Technicians install radios, radar equipment, displays, controls, crew amenities and so on, like surgeons transplanting new organs into a patient. The wiring and ducts provide power and sustenance in just the way that blood supplies circulate within the human body.

LEFT Marconi Avionics development engineers tested AEW Nimrod systems on a fully representative ground rig. The communication officer position is prominent in this view, his controls extending into the roof area, and teleprinters separate him from the navigator

ABOVE AEW Nimrod radar operators have identical consoles. Equipment was installed in the development aircraft in time for test-flights to commence in 1979

The flight deck is a three-man workshop for pilot, co-pilot and flight engineer. At a first glance the differences from a Nimrod MR.2 panels are so minor as to be indistinguishable. It is intriguing to see that the crew still has a weather radar display, identical to an airliner unit, but the radar, instead of being in the nose, is grafted onto the front of the starboard wing slipper tank. From the windows the large front radome is almost invisible, so crew field-of-view has not been compromised for the radar's sake.

Aft of the flight deck the crew entry door is on the starboard side (Soviet style!) and it faces the forward cooling pack and part of the navigator's console. The latter is larger than any other operator's station as it has a flat chart table. Above the table is the navigation-position display projector, which the navigator can slew using controls at the upper right-hand corner of the desk. He also has radio controllers and an impressive vertical bank of navigation system controls. His primary navigation sensors are two Ferranti FIN1012 inertial navigation sets (each identical to those used in Nimrod MR.2s).

Separating the navigator from what are then six almost identical operator's positions are two radio teletypes and a punch-tape reader, which are accessible to the communications control officer. He will occupy the most forward operator position which, additional to the displays and controls fitted in all other positions, has also a sloping eye-height communications system master control panel. The latter provides control over a communication system combining LF/HF/VHF/UHF voice link and comprises some 120 separate avionics boxes. Control is vested in a system called Auto-Management of Radio and Intercom by Computer (Amrics), and the development of this system was a Marconi Avionics, Basildon, responsibility. It is a vital system and its development timetable tended to lead all other systems. As soon as new facilities were added during development the Amrics systems was expected to be ready to cope with the additional communication traffic that might be generated.

Communication equipment testing started in a standard Nimrod in early 1978, over two years ahead of most other airborne system development. US-designed Collins Link 11 radio communication is to be used at first, all the equipment being licence-built and integrated with other systems by Marconi Avionics. By the time that a representative airframe was flying, in late 1979, there were three communication systems in use, one at the manufacturer's plant, one at Radlett where the main development rig was located, and the third in the trials Nimrod.

The Joint Tactical Information Distribution System (Jtids) described in detail in Chapter 5 embodies the latest in radio communications thinking and has reflected all Nato's requirements. The Royal Aircraft Establishment at Farnborough has been very closely associated with UK requirements and by the time this book is read its involvement in obtaining US-built prototype terminals, testing them, and paving the path for UK production of Jtids equipment should have passed its peak. If the whole plan operates smoothly both RAF-operated Nimrod AEW.3s and Nato-operated Boeing E-3s will be Jtids-equipment at the same time, and therefore totally interoperable in Nato airspace.

The five most aft operator's positions are identical. Four are used by radar operators and one by the ESM system operator. Each man faces a 30 cm (12 in) diameter display with a rectangular alpha-numeric data display to his right. On the table in front of him the operator has a traditional keyboard, fitted with a few extra functions, and a set of radar selection switches. By his left hand is a rolling-ball control which can be used to position a cursor on the main display. Controls along the bottom of the console allow different scales and display offsets to be selected, as required, and in normal operation the display will show a north-orientated ground-stabilized map. Communications controls are arranged in a stack on the operator's left-hand side.

Serious attempts to make the operator's task as easy as possible were reflected in the specification in ways which were exemplified earlier. To ensure that all the functions required were integrated, and that a full system would not pose any more problems than could be probed on the ground, a complete system rig was set-up by Marconi Avionics at Radlett in Hertfordshire. The rig is complete even to the extent of having radar antennas at each end of a floor space laid out in identical fashion to the aircraft cabin. The radar naturally cannot radiate, but wherever possible simulations are used to close control loops and the system operation can mimic actual aircraft missions almost exactly.

On each display the operator can be provided with a background map which shows coastlines and other essential features, and all requested target data. A line streaming behind each target symbol shows track history and gives an indication of speed. Identification data is selectable, and can be shown on targets of interest. Extra data is provided to operator's on the alpha-numeric displays, the appropriate tables of infor-

mation being available after laying a cursor on the target location. Latest position is shown by a symbol, which was a diamond initially, but during development was changed to a hexagon shape. The symbol is complete if radar, IFF, ESM and radio-communication data is available on a target. Symbol completeness immediately indicates to what degree the target is understood.

Radar information is combined with Identification Friend or Foe (IFF) data before it reaches the operator. The two systems share antennas but use totally different processors. Cossor developed the IFF system used in AEW Nimrod. The third sensor, the ESM system, is designed by Loral, a US manufacturer, and production of many of its components is carried out by MEL in Britain. The ESM antennas are in wing-tip pods which have oblique nose and tail profiles, there being four antennas behind each face. The total array of 16 antennas provides wide waveband reception and a 360° field of view. When incoming data has been unravelled, and in this respect the system is similar in operation to the E-2C passive-detection system, it is compared with a catalogue of data in a threat library which resides in the ESM processor unit. If automatic correlation is difficult the ESM operator will be provided with information on his alphanumeric display, and he will attempt to identify the target.

Aft of the operators are a few avionics cabinets containing the mission recorder and some communications equipment. These butt against a bulkhead which divides the operators from a stretch of fuselage extending about 8 m (26 ft) over the wing centre-section which is lined on both sides with electronic equipment. Their specific functions are too wide-ranging to be considered individually, but it is here where the radar transmitter and receiver, IFF, ESM, central data-processing and the bulk of communications hardware is located.

The radar transmitter is located on the starboard side of the aircraft and has two waveguides, one to each radar antenna. Radiation losses in these long connections represent a sizeable disbenefit, but the disadvantages are regarded as a small penalty by British radar gurus, who point out that all the radiation eventually emitted goes

British Aerospace engineers at Woodford are producing eleven AEW Nimrods by modifying the fore and aft sections of standard Nimrods that are surplus to RAF maritime reconnaissance requirements. Like the puppet that has told a lie, a Nimrod grows a long nose

Most extensive airframe modification is the addition of a new rear fuselage aft of the pressure bulkhead and revised empennage

out unimpeded. The transmitter radiation is switched between waveguides as each antenna completes its 180° scan. A two-stage travelling-wave tube (TWT) transmitter generates coherent pulses at the required pulse repetition frequency (PRF), which can be either medium-PRF for overland operations, or low-PRF for overwater use. A blend of the two can be introduced when sectors across land and sea are being searched.

To dissipate the large amount of heat generated by all the equipment two cooling systems are installed. That associated with the radar transmitter pumps a fluoro-carbon fluid around the TWTs. Although this is an expensive coolant, the fluid has good dielectric properties and it can be piped close to the various stages of the TWTs.

Most of the remaining avionics system is cooled by a water-glycol system which draws excess heat from hollow shelves, called cold-plates, on which the various avionics boxes are tightly clamped. The excess heat is taken to two heat-exchangers in the lower aft fuselage where it is transferred to fuel. The fuel is pumped to and from the outer wing fuel tanks, using as pipes the top-hat stringer sections which are bonded to the inner wing surface. Heat is eventually dissipated from the fuel-tank walls, but addition-

ally, to safeguard operations when the aircraft is parked in direct sunlight or involved in prolonged ground-running, a high-capacity ground trolley can be connected to cope with the cooling requirements.

Vital to the operation of any sizeable avionics system, but invisible once it has been built and installed in its cabinets, is the philosophy adopted in respect of processor relationships. AEW Nimrod avionics systems were the subjects of project definition in the mid-1970s, and this was late enough to take advantage of microprocessor technology and produced a distributed processing system. The central computer, which is called the integrated data processor, is still a fairly bulky affair, and is developed from the GEC 4080M computer. It is large enough, and fast enough, to conduct all the basic sensor correlation and track file maintenance tasks. In this processor alone there is about 1000 kilo-byte (8-bit words) of storage. More importantly, the integrated data-processor links to the operator's consoles and other systems, whenever possible, by daisy-chain connections, called a data-bus by engineers. Fourty-five individual microproces-

The massive forward-facing inverted-cassagrain antenna is supported on a rigid structural extension so that it has an uninterrupted sweep through 180°

sors are connected in this way, contributing another 1400 kilo-byte of storage, and they are the key to making data available to operators and other systems within a short time of a request being made. The central computer is like a boiler supplying hot water, and the microprocessors are like little vats which dispense coffee, tea or cocoa, as requested. Supplying the raw ingredients, electronically at least, is the way that the central computer programming task was isolated, and kept to a manageable proportion, and it is envisaged that as the system grows that only microprocessor software changes will be needed to fine-tune the system. Marconi Avionics estimates that by the time the full 2.4 mega-byte system has been programmed, over 300,000 man-hours will have been spent by its software-engineering team alone.

In the final section of the AEW Nimrod fuselage, aft of all the technical masterpieces, are the mundane crew rest facilities. There is a small vestibule with tables and seats, lifejacket stowage cabinets, a rear door with an emergency chute, a generous baggage compartment, wardrobe, and a toilet and washroom. Unlike the US Air Force, which encourages its crews to relax in bunks when off duty, the RAF has not asked for any sleeping facilities. For normal operations, mis-

sions of 10 hours maximum, this is a fair assumption, but if in-flight refuelling capability becomes standard, and the prospect of 24-hour missions increases, there must be a good chance of that sizeable baggage (duty-free loot?) space being converted into a sleeping area.

So far, the AEW radar has been mentioned only in passing on this project, and there are many who believe that it should be treated simply as a sensor and not pulled out for specific attention. While this might reflect the operational aspects of AEW operation, it does not illustrate just how much effort has been put into the radar system. It has been one of the most challenging of all UK avionics development programmes.

The configuration, using fore and aft antennas to obtain an uninterrupted view all around the aircraft is unique. The sequencing of operations is controlled centrally, each antenna being swept through 180° in about 5 seconds, then reversed at a slightly faster speed so that it is positioned to take on another scan when the other aerial has completed its own scan. The attributes of the inverted-cassegrain antennas are dealt with in the chapter on radar technology. Any other nation

This photograph of AEW Nimrod radar-data-processor equipment in build emphasises the vast amount of cooling air that has to be pumped through the equipment bays

would have probably chosen the slotted-wave-guide antenna which is used in the Boeing E-3, but Elliott engineers have grown fond of the inverted-cassegrain, and believe that because it is less sensitive to frequency variations, they can operate the radar over a wider bandwidth, thus making the radar system less easy to deceive with radar jammers. They claim also that the sidelobe performance is equivalent to what a large slotted wave-guide antenna, of Boeing E-3 proportions, can achieve. The dual-beam height-finding technique used in AEW-Nimrod is often scorned by slotted-waveguide adherents, and their observation that phase-shifter controlled beam steering can measure the height of low-altitude targets more accurately is probably true. But British engineers will always point out that their technique does not cause the radar to 'squint', so it does not develop large sidelobes, albeit that this only happens temporarily with a slotted-wave-guide aerial. Comparative arguments are in fact valueless, because in every design exercise of this magnitude the compromises are numerous, the operating requirements vary enormously, and they often depend on how the customer is willing to rate the value of different attributes against different viewpoints. Even so, it will be interesting to hear, in due course, how operators rate the comparative performances of the AEW Nimrod and Boeing E-3A radars in European conditions.

Quite apart from the radiating hardware, the British radar processor is something of which its designers are again very proud, and it is here where a tremendous investment in money and manpower has been staked. The pulse-Doppler receiver occupies three cabinets in the AEW Nimrod centre section, and in these are packed banks of digitally-controlled filters which extract frequency-spectrum data from received radiation. A Marconi 920ATC computer then analyzes the filter bank outputs. The computer uses fast-Fourier Transforms (FFT), a speciality of signal-processing engineers.

A mathematical thesis would be necessary to reveal all that happens, but in essence the program is structured to use a complex algebraic technique called Fourier Transform, which might be familiar to some readers, to unravel the filter bank data. As real Fourier Transforms are tedious calculations that cannot be completed in the time available, a subtly modified equivalent algorithm is used to complete the job faster, and with adequate accuracy. It would be difficult to

AEW Nimrod sits in the hangar at Woodford completing its final acceptance checks before delivery

put a price on the value to Britain of maintaining an indigenous capability of this nature. Several of the UK MoD research establishments, the Royal Signals and Radar Establishment (RSRE) at Great Malvern, and the Royal Aircraft Establishment (RAE) at Farnborough, in particular, have proposed or inspired this kind of building block over the last couple of decades and deserve credit for contributing to what industry uses in its high-technology equipment.

It should be emphasized that techniques such as FFT are not unique to AEW Nimrod, but are fundamental to many signal-processing operations. There are many other equivalent and fascinating examples of engineering ingenuity which are hidden in AEW Nimrod's computers, and it is a sad fact that they are often too complex and so totally invisible that their designers cannot earn the credit due to them. This is something that has to be said about AEW design generally, and I have reserved comment on the topic until near the end of the three major AEW aircraft descriptions. The same stories are as inextricably hidden in the Grumman E-2 and Boeing E-3

In sideview AEW Nimrod can look surprisingly sleek, but its uncompromising duty to patrol the skies as a long-range snooper is clearly evident

Aircraft in service with the Royal Air Force have a new low-visibility camouflage scheme, which can do nothing to really disguise the AEW Nimrod's distinctive profile

after 1973 and never delivered to the Royal Air Force, and three more aircraft were withdrawn from service after the disbanding of No. 203 maritime reconnaissance squadron, which had been based in Malta.

This made the production task straight-forward. There has been little more to do than lop off the nose and tail, and graft AEW protruberences onto existing metal. The internal fixes are considerable of course, and even extend to installing a new electrical generation system, comprising a 48 kW alternator on each engine; two for the radar (on the outer engines), and two for the avionics (on the inner engines). The simplicity of the programme has kept costs down, but new airframe production will call for a lot of re-jigging, which will be very expensive, and this makes AEW Nimrod less attractive than it could be to potential overseas customers. It is a classic case of Britain looking after her own requirements, militarily, and at unbelievably modest expense, but failing at the same time to fulfil the requirements for a programme that could be profitable in the long-term.

The aircraft is irredeemably linked to UK requirements, including fairy-tale cost objectives. Without the latter, and therefore with a sensible price to support an overseas marketing strategy, AEW Nimrod could have helped towards the real objective of aircraft manufacture—to make money. It seems highly unlikely that any AEW Nimrods, beyond those being built for RAF use, will ever be manufactured.

developments, and deserve as much admiration.

Aircraft programmes are never static, and just as airlines will change their timetables from year to year to match changes in passenger demands, military objectives change with time too, and can affect aircraft programmes. Throughout its development AEW Nimrod was geared to low-level aircraft detection over maritime areas around Europe, and this was assessed to be possible with 11 aircraft. This coincidentally equalled the number of Nimrod airframes in Britain which were not in service. Eight aircraft had been built

All 11 UK-operated AEW Nimrods are to be based at RAF Waddington in Lincolnshire, and they will carry out duties from satellite bases as necessary. The primary role will involve patrols at between 200 and 700 nm from base, with up to 9 hours on station. Endurance will rarely need to exceed 10 hours.

After the Falklands crisis in 1982 however, this supposition needed some re-assessment. Provision for in-flight refuelling, which had always been available, was added to aircraft as they were being built. Missions of 24 hours or so endurance no longer seemed only remotely possible, and hence additional features such as sleeping accommodation will need to be incorporated. In an aircraft which has some 400 individually-replaceable electronic boxes, and even with exceptional reliability, the chances of maintaining a reasonable servicability throughout a 24-hour mission will be very remote. The easy solution is to carry more spare electronic units on the aircraft, so that more in-flight replacements can be initiated. The British aircraft does not currently carry a radar maintenance engineer, and yet he would find equipment more accessible than his counterpart in the Boeing E-3. If longer sorties do become more frequent, an extra technician crewman to tweek the 'wiggly amps' is a very real possibility.

Finally, in conjunction with the technical nature of the aircraft systems, there are lessons to be learned from other AEW aircraft, and the Falklands factor. Self-defence now seems sure to be introduced. Britain fitted AIM-9L Side-winder air-to-air missiles to its Nimrod MR.2s during the Falkland Crisis, on the off chance that meeting an unarmed Argentinian Boeing 707 on similar duties would result in a kill. The case for doing the same on AEW Nimrod is just as easy to justify.

Britain's AEW Nimrod production programme officially started after the programme go-ahead was announced on 31 March 1977. The first structurally complete aircraft was rolled-out on 30 March 1980, and it first flew on 16 July with Charles Masefield and Johnny Cruse crewing the aircraft. They reported total satisfaction with its handling after a $3\frac{1}{2}$ hour assessment. The large radomes hardly affect directional stability, and all flight regimes they considered are less problematical than the bomb-doors open configuration of the Nimrod MR.2. Six months later, in January 1981, the second production aircraft joined the programme, and this was used for airborne development of the mission avionics system, including the radar.

The RAF worked feverishly to convert Waddington from a Vulcan base to being Nimrod compatible by late-1982, and aircraft should be entering service there as this book is published. By late-1985 all 11 RAF Nimrod AEW.3s should be in service.

After the Falkland Islands campaign in 1982, when RAF Nimrods made long surveillance flights over the South Atlantic, AEW Nimrod trials were conducted with an in-flight refuelling probe installed

Chapter 10
Soviet AEW

If the considered opinion of Western analysts in the 1960s was that their nations needed AEW aircraft to counter possible Soviet threats, it seems reasonable to expect that in the same period Soviet analysts considered an equivalent aircraft to be a suitable addition to their air force too. At what date the Russian-built Tu-126 Moss was conceived, when it entered operational service, and with what success it operates, are not facts that are easy to determine.

It would seem that some time in the mid-1960s, while the US and Britain pontificated seriously about a land-based AEW-type, the Soviets characteristically got on with the job. Certainly, it appears that sometime around 1967 they first flew an aerodynamic prototype, and hence while the US was wrapped in the Overland Radar Technology project, and Britain was delving into the intricasies of FMICW radars, the Soviets were already flying a big aircraft, aiming to fulfil similar mission requirements.

Given that an AEW type is only required in relatively small numbers, and also that it has to be a fairly large aircraft with long endurance at high altitude, Soviet designers drew the same conclusions as their Western counterparts; that it is natural to assess the potential of an existing airframe rather than to develop a totally new aircraft. Soviet designers would have faced a choice something like the list shown on page 152.

The two outstanding types were the Antonov An-22 and Tupolev Tu-114, as both can manage to stay aloft much longer than any other type. Both are turboprop-powered however, and, as the Hawkeye story has revealed, this can impose difficulties, although not insuperable, that a jet or turbofan-powered type does not face. Inevitably, the Ilyushin Il-62 with its four turbofans and ten hours or so maximum endurance would have been a tempting basic airframe, but we know now that this type was in the throes of an agonizing development programme, and has never adequately lived up to expectations.

Of the two turboprop types, the Antonov An-22 was so new (it had first flown on 27 February 1965) that an airframe was unlikely to be avail-

An unusual view of a Tupolev Tu-126 Moss shows that a single broad pylon supports the deep rotodome assembly. Blister on the forward fuselage is thought to enclose a satellite antenna, and blisters on rear fuselage could be for passive-detection systems

Side view of Tupolev Tu-126 Moss shows how AEW appendages marr the lines of a once beautiful airliner. The large metal contra-rotating propellors stand-out clearly

able quickly. On the other hand, the Tu-114 was an airliner which was proven, it was about the right size, and a few spare examples might have been available. A radome and support design almost identical to that tested on the Lockheed WV-2E in the late-1950s was adopted, and in 1969 the Soviet authorities created a minor panic in various US DoD offices when they released a propaganda film which gave a tantilizing glimpse of what appeared to be a Tu-114 with an 11 m (36 ft) diameter rotodome mounted above the rear fuselage. This was the first officially-ack-

nowledged evidence of a Soviet AEW aircraft, and it was the type which has subsequently become known as the Tu-126 Moss.

Although Tu-126s are shrouded in secrecy, the Tu-114 airliner was the well-respected flagship of the Aeroflot fleet for about half a decade, and familiar to Westerners. Amongst other aircraft it always looked magnificent because it towered 16 m (52 ft) to the top of the fin. This was partly due to its long and immensely strong-looking undercarriage. Indeed, whenever a Tu-114 visited the Paris Air Show in the 1960s, it was the only aircraft of the era that people could walk under; and its 311 m^2 (3349 ft^2) wing was a great shelter when the inevitable shower tipped over Le Bourget.

A designer would normally shun such a massive and heavy undercarriage arrangement of

powerplant, giving 32 blades in total on each aircraft. This mass of whirling ironmongery, as much as the aircraft's sheer size, enhanced its enigmatic character.

But those huge windmills are the Achilles heel of the Tu-126; they are made of metal, and to a modern radar they present a radar-reflecting surface equivalent to an airborne battleship. The Tu-20 Bear, now used in the Tu-95 variant as an electronic-intelligence gathering aircraft around Western shores, is perhaps the most identifiable radar target in service. On some early airborne-interception radars with rudimentary pulse-Doppler receivers the aircraft is immediately recognizable by the string of lines which march with the main target return, each one representing a ghost echo generated in the Doppler analyzer by harmonics set-up in the propellor discs. Trying to hide any large aircraft in electrically-generated clutter is always difficult, but with the Tu-114 and related types, it is simply impossible.

The propellors, merely a few feet below and ahead of the radar antenna on the Tu-126, would be just as capable of upsetting it's receiver, if it was a pulse-Doppler type, as they are of giving their distinctive signature to similar types of radars. Indeed, irrespective of whether or not the Tu-126 uses a pulse-Doppler receiver, they must have presented problems of enormous magnitudes for the Soviet radar designers.

Pulse-Doppler technology was a distant concept at the time that the first Tu-126 was constructed, and it can have hardly been conceivable as a candidate radar technique. It is more likely that Soviet engineers were emulating what was known of the E-2 Hawkeye system and had chosen to mimic the AN/APS-111 AMTI system. With the sort of electronic capability credited to the Soviet Union in that period it would not have been impossible for a radar of this type to be installed in a Tu-126, and it might have been capable of detecting ships and large aircraft out to the radar horizon.

Some updating of the system can be reasonably assumed during the 1970s, perhaps improving the detection range against smaller aircraft targets. US intelligence still claims that the Tu-126 cannot see aircraft flying low overland, and this does suggest that a fairly simple form of AMTI is being used. It is however, generally accepted that detection performance against low-flying targets overwater is reasonably good.

The Tu-126 is clearly a conversion of the Tu-114 airliner. In some quarters it is believed that all Tu-126s are newly-built airframes, not merely

course, but other matters had forced Tupolev to accept the weight penalty. The Tu-114 had a low wing and underslung engine nacelles. The wing also had a small amount of anhedral, and consequently the centrelines of all four engine nacelles, viewed from the side, were approximately in-line with the fuselage keel. The long undercarriage was needed to provide the full blade length of each massive, 5.6 m (18.3 ft) diameter, contra-rotating propellor plus ground clearance. It still seems incredible that each of the 12,000 eshp Kuznetsov NK-12M turboprop engines installed in the Tu-114 is approximately as powerful as all four engines on the largest contemporary Western turboprop airliner design. Indeed, it was because of the enormous amount of power transmitted by each engine that two contra-rotating four-bladed propellors were installed on each

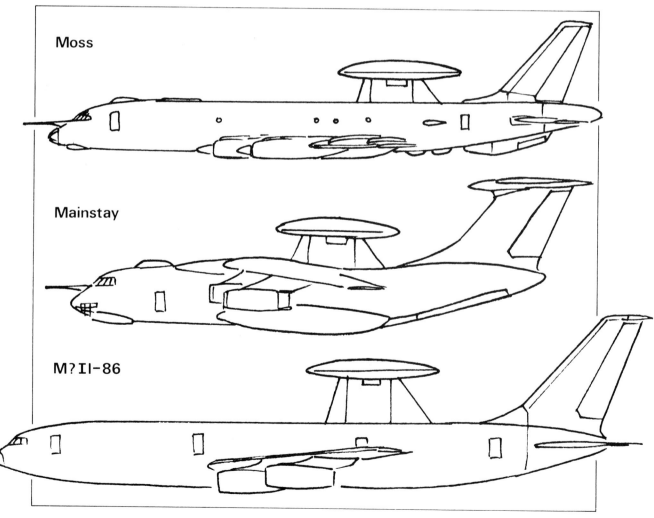

Moss

Mainstay

M?Il-86

LEFT The original airliner, Tu-114 Cleat, was a graceful pre-jet creation. It combined swept wings with turboprop engines

ABOVE Modern successor to Tu-114 is the Ilyushin Il-86 Camber airliner, which is seen to be a logical basic airframe for future AEW operations

The drawings here show, to scale, several existing, rumoured and proposed Soviet AEW aircraft configurations. A slimmer rotodome might be used on the newer aircraft, but there is no photographic evidence to support either the Il-76 or Il-86 AEW project

refurbished Tu-114s, although with only a few of the type in existence, and as the 30-aircraft Aeroflot Tu-114 fleet was run down quite rapidly in the 1967–1970 period when Tu-126s appeared, an airliner conversion programme seems to have been likely. The broad pressurized hull of the airliner was obviously advantageous for accommodating the airborne-control crew and the large amount of radar and communications equipment.

Only some 10–12 examples of Tu-126, and certainly no more than 20, are thought to have been in service at any time, and it has been widely claimed that the conversion programme was completed several years ago. This raises a lot of speculation about whether the Tu-126 will be replaced in the near future, and if so, what airframe will be used. A few years ago the most widely favoured candidate was the Ilyushin Il-86 Camber, an airframe with Boeing 707 proportions,

but wide-bodied, which could accommodate a rotodome on top of the rear fuselage. The type is widely rumoured, but at the time of printing there had been no sightings by any intelligence source that was willing to talk about it. Delays could have been incurred by the rush to supply examples of the prestigious wide-bodied Il-86 to Aeroflot in time for the Olympic games, which were held in Moscow during 1980.

Meanwhile, several US magazines have carried reports, and in one case an artist's impression, based on alleged US DoD satellite reconnaissance data, of a rotodome-equipped Ilyushin Il-76 Candid military transport. In that it is an established design, already in service with the Soviet military, this makes a lot of sense.

It must be assumed that Soviet technicians are now working with pulse-Doppler radar, if only because the technology is implied by the operational capabilities of new fighters and strike types. The Il-76 would be a much better test-platform than the Tu-126, in that it does not have a forest of propellor blades, but even so the Il-76 airframe is far from ideal. The wing centre-section forms a large reflecting surface relatively close to the antenna, and corner reflections from the T-tail configuration, whatever the radar technology, will create plenty of nightmarish problems. It may be safe to presume that the Il-76 AEW variant is an experimental pulse-Doppler system, but that in the long-term a rotodome-equipped Il-86 will most likely replace the Tu-126.

Meanwhile, a few of the Tu-126 systems have been clearly identified. It is likely that the roto-dome encloses a Yagi-antenna array, not dissimilar to that used on the E-2 Hawkeye. Certainly the Tu-126 was introduced too early to have a slotted-waveguide antenna, and a retrofit is unlikely to have occurred.

Standard SRO-2M IFF transponder equipment, evident because of the distinctive 'organ-pipe' antennas, and used in most Soviet front-line aircraft is installed, plus Sirena III 360°-azimuth coverage radar-warning system. No defensive armament or electronic-passive warning equipment has been positively identified, although there are numerous blisters on the fuselage which could cover passive-detection antennas. An IFF interrogation capability is implicit in the nature of AEW operations.

It is believed that in view of the large cabin volume available, that the Soviets have adopted the airborne command-post concept, and that there are several operator positions plus a wide range of operating facilities. Communications systems include VHF, UHF, HF and datalink (probably VHF), and the fuselage tail cone is similar to that fitted to Tu-95s which can trail a long VLF radio antenna. It is not clear whether VLF radio transmissions, which are invariably to submarines, do take place.

The navigation system has been deduced to employ an inertial navigation set for operations between fixes, and an RSBN-20 short-range navigation system for stand-by use. A navigation computer which can provide best navigation data from all radio and inertial sensors has been claimed. Miscellaneous equipment also includes a radio altimeter and a VOR/ILS radio-navaid receiver. A crew complement of 12 is often reported, but some sources suggest that Tu-126 carries 17 crewmen. The latter is more consistent with full airborne command-post operations using the sort of technology available in the Soviet Union. It would not be inconsistent with other examples of Soviet technology from the same period to assume that the basic aircraft has relatively limited automatic-tracking capacity, and that manual operations in support of track identification and initiation will be high.

No clear pattern of Tu-126 deployment has emerged with the aircraft already reported in service. First known operation involved one aircraft in 1971, which assisted the Indian air force to monitor Pakistani air movements, and in 1980 Tu-126s were reported to be monitoring aircraft

The Tupolev Tu-95 Bear is an intelligence-gathering aircraft which has the same wings and powerplants as Tu-126, but uses the slim fuselage of the Tu-20 Bear bomber

LEFT The Ilyushin Il-76 Candid transport aircraft is the unlikely, but widely rumoured, airframe used for Soviet AEW equipment trials. A rotodome is mounted above the wing trailing-edge on reported AEW variant, and will have severe antenna blockage problems

movements around the borders of Afghanistan. These were both overland operations, and in view of the alleged poor overland capability of the radar, the reports do not stand up to close scrutiny. Most reported operations seem to take place intermittently overwater, and especially on the Baltic and Pacific approaches to Soviet ports, where surface and submerged vessel activity is naturally monitored very diligently. More aircraft may be introduced to monitor sensitive overland approaches to the Soviet Union and Warsaw Pact nations close to Western Europe as soon as a pulse-Doppler radar is available. This step forward is most likely to be signalled by the observation of rotodome-equipped Il-76 or Il-86 aircraft, an event that has been speculated about for many years.

Presuming that Soviet engineers are proceed-

Soviet airframes suitable for AEW use

Aircraft	Engines	Max weight (kg)	Cruise speed/ht (kts)/(ft)	Max endurance (hrs)
Antonov An-10/12	4 × turboprops	61,000	340/33,000	8
Antonov An-22	4 × turboprops	250,000	370/30,000	16
Ilyushin Il-18	4 × turboprops	64,000	340/33,000	11
Ilyushin Il-62	4 × turbofans	157,000	470/36,000	10
Tupolev Tu-16	2 × turbojets	68,000	420/35,000	8
Tupolev Tu-104	2 × turbojets	76,000	430/33,000	5
Tupolev Tu-114	4 × turboprops	175,000	415/29,500	13
Tupolev Tu-154	3 × turbofans	80,000	460/36,000	7

ing with a co-ordinated pulse-Doppler radar development programme, and have given priority to the introduction of look-down/shoot-down capability to a new generation of defensive aircraft, a pulse-Doppler equipped Soviet AEW type could be expected to be in service by 1985.

Then would be the time to look out for the new aircraft in the vicinity of Western Europe and the Middle East, and its arrival would coincide with the commencement of fully-integrated operations in the same regions by the equivalently capable Boeing E-3A and Nimrod AEW.3.

Chapter 11
AEW Survival

If you were an airman assigned to fly airborne-early warning missions in one of the types now in service, your interest would be more than superficially aroused by the question of AEW survivability. There can be few more potentially hazardous jobs in an air force or navy; yet because this is not always obvious in peacetime operations there is a temptation for the survivability questions to be hidden from public view.

Self-defence was first mentioned in respect of provision made for an armament hardpoint on the Boeing E-3, (which came about only after Nato had ordered the aircraft) and which has been retrofitted to US Air Force aircraft more recently. Additionally, in 1983 the Royal Air Force acknowledged that its existing Nimrod MR.2 fleet could carry up to four Sidewinder AIM-9L air-to-air missiles on underwing

pylons, and the implication is that Nimrod AEW.3s will have the same capability. E-2C Hawkeye is not acknowledged to have any self-defence capability and there has been no official indication yet on whether the Soviets have incorporated self-defence features in the Tu-126 and prospective replacement types.

An AEW aircraft on patrol is vulnerable. It is bound to be close to the boundaries within which friendly forces operate, although closeness in this respect is a relative term. Generally an AEW will be 100–150 nm from where the enemy has established his own front-lines, and a typical AEW flight pattern will cause the aircraft to cruise roughly parallel to this boundary, at between 300–400 kts.

The sort of weapon that is likely to be used against an AEW type by any attacking fighter would be a medium-range air-to-air missile, which can be fired from 15 to 25 nm away. The spread of effective missile range is created by relative target motion. If it is moving away, for example, the missile has to be released at a closer range than if it was moving towards the aggressor. There are points for and against all aspects of attack. From the aggressors point of view, a head-on attack, while opening the possibility of releasing a weapon at longer range, does

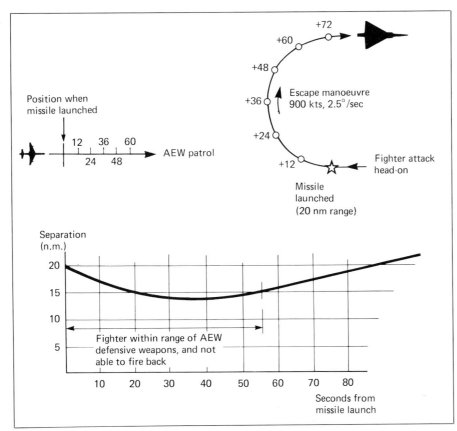

AEW survivability
A very simple attack geometry is shown here. It illustrates how a supersonic fighter, attempting a head-on attack (which means it can release missiles at their maximum effective range) can itself be very vulnerable to action which the AEW aircraft might take to defend itself. The AEW aircraft will have detected the fighter much earlier than the fighter detected it, so although it is a slow and unmanoeuvrable type an AEW clearly is not necessarily an easy target

involve a more hazardous escape manoeuvre than an attack from behind. It is hazardous to the fighter because during the escape the AEW will be behind the aircraft and therefore, usually, invisible to his radar. The distance between aircraft will be less than the maximum release distance of the missile used for a period of perhaps two minutes after missile launch. In addition, the fighter is likely to be manoeuvring as hard as possible, and if it is using reheat, it will be an easy target for any infrared heat-seeking weapon which the AEW might launch.

Analyses of various engagement geometries tend to lead to the inescapable conclusion that if all the points for and against are taken into account, and balanced according to the relative values of various capabilities, the AEW is always well placed. The reason why this pedestrian aircraft can acquit itself, even against high-speed attackers with the longest-range weapons available, is because it can be confident of knowing any aggressor's movements long before the aircraft is close enough to be a threat. Any attacker should have been detected and categorized as a potential threat a long time before it got close enough to be an actual threat, and therefore should be susceptible to action which the AEW takes to defend itself. AEW survivability depends almost entirely on the variety of actions which an AEW aircraft can take, and in general the greater the breadth of possibilities open to any crew, the greater are their chances of survival.

Protection is more difficult over the sea than over land, and AEWs operating off carriers provide clear examples of how to plan for survival. A powerful naval force at sea will often observe strict radio silence, relying on covert operations to maintain an element of surprise. It does not necessarily therefore want to keep an aircraft circling overhead, spraying radar signals in all directions that are easily detectable at 500 nm range by a high-flying electronic-intelligence (Elint) aircraft. It would be rather like setting up a radio beacon and broadcasting one's presence. AEW operations off carriers have to be disguised as much as possible. Reference has been made already to the way that US Navy crews will often cruise for several minutes at low level before beginning their climb to patrol altitude. Recovery can follow the same procedure. When on patrol the AEW will not fly simply in a circle around the ships it is trying to protect, but it will describe a pattern chosen to maximize the probability of target detection in zones from where attackers can be expected, while also ensuring that signifi-

cant blank areas are not opened up, exposing the ships to unexpected attacks from other quarters.

If unfriendly aircraft and ships are about the AEW may not use its radar continuously. This is one reason why the US Navy was quick to recognize the value of a passive-detection system (PDS). The E-2C Hawkeye can switch its radar to stand-by and listen for any electro-magnetic messages which may indicate enemy activity by using its PDS. When it is necessary to conduct roles other than enemy detection, such as assisting in the recovery of aircraft returning to the fleet, the radar will be used for only a short period during each rotation of the antenna, care being taken to radiate only in directions where if detected the radar will not destroy any chance of surprise. Care must be taken of course to ensure that radiation which leaks out in sidelobes does not produce a detectable signal, and this is yet another good reason for sidelobes to be as small as possible on any kind of AEW system.

There is always the chance that a 'quiet' aircraft or ship, which has taken care to not radiate any radar or radio messages will penetrate an AEW veil if the radar is not used, so occasional sweeps are made, even on covert missions. Just when these sweeps are made, and what the aircraft does to disguise its track between sweeps, are essential considerations if its future position is not to be predicted easily, and it is all a matter of operational experience.

A typical US Navy operation with an E-2C Hawkeye located 200 nm from its carrier, and when the fleet is intent on surprising an enemy, will call for it to conduct covert operations, except perhaps in a sector over the friendly forces. At all times the PDS will be collecting and identifying radio transmissions, and locating them as accurately as possible. For example, if radar emissions which suggest a known type of enemy ship are detected in the covert region of coverage this information can be correlated with other intelligence before the radar is used to scan the area of interest. The correlation can be conducted on-board the carrier, where information has probably been received by secure datalink, or if the data is available on the aircraft, intelligence operations can be conducted within the Hawkeye itself. The latter is preferrable, as if the

The first of the modern AEW types to be associated with survival tactics, in public debate, was the Nato-operated Boeing E-3 fleet. It was ordered with a hardpoint in the wing inner leading-edge to accommodate air-to-air missiles. However, this is rarely mentioned, and the aircraft has not been photographed with armaments attached

E-2C is having to transmit radio data to the carrier it will compromise its own silent patrol, but getting all the appropriate receiver and processing capability on-board may not always be possible. Survivability is intrinsically linked to the degree of on-board processing that can be accommodated.

At some time the decision has to be taken to turn-on the radar, thereby giving away the presence of an AEW aircraft. The aircraft's presence will now indicate a real threat to any unfriendly force, as although an AEW type cannot launch an attack itself, the information that it is gathering will indicate that an attack from the fleet with which it operates is possible, and perhaps imminent.

Hence, once the cat-and-mouse game has been played thoroughly, and every bit of surprise wrung out of the tactical situation, covertness goes by the board. If both sides use AEW aircraft, there will be no pretence to disguise them. The signal to turn the radars on would probably be taken after the PDS used by one side has detected a pattern of activities which suggested that action was imminent by the other, so again

it is common practice to inject as much randomness as possible into everyday operations. In this way snoopers will not be suspicious until the very last moment. This is not an easy objective when one thinks of the defensive radars, missile acquisition radars and IFF code procedures, to mention only a few time-ordered features that can broadcast news of a build-up to an attack.

After the point of operating continuously as a fleet look-out has been passed, an AEW with no defensive armament has only two options. To ensure its survival it must see that it is close enough to the fleet's defensive umbrella to slip under cover before any potential threat can get sufficiently close to attack, or it must have dedicated interceptor cover. The latter can often be available automatically if interceptors are up to protect friendly bombers or on combat air patrol.

When a seaborne force knows that its position

Seen together at Seattle, not in Europe, a Nato/Boeing E-3 is accompanied by a General Dynamics F-16 fighter. It is not a coincidence that European deployment of the E-3 has been preceded by such fighter types, which act co-operatively to attack enemy aircraft entering the field of surveillance, and to protect the large AEW aircraft

is obvious, the survivability procedures used are exactly analogous to those connected with border patrols by land-based AEW types. Large land-based types depend a lot on having interceptors close at hand to provide protection, but in the last resort instead of roaring off towards the carrier position, they will strike towards landbases which have interceptor squadrons available. This is a last resort, as to relinquish the patrol line does infer that one has lost control over sky in which air-superiority was sought. The fighters and interceptors have to regain control of this air-space again as soon as possible; and that could be easier said than done.

Survival has been projected above as being very dependent on stealthy operations. This side of warfare never impresses as much as supersonic jets dashing about the sky at extremely high speed, shooting off expensive pieces of rocketry and totting up kills like latter-day Baron Von Richthofens. But it is a method of fighting that will be instantly recognized by realists. If Tom and Jerry fought each other every minute of every day in the manner that cartoons would have us believe, they would have to be exceptionally fit

animals. We accept the idiomatic side of cartoon characters, and tend to forget the stalking and baiting the real cats and mice play. The men of AEW squadrons are trained to appreciate the realistic approach. Their fighter colleagues might go gung-ho for five minutes a couple of times in each peacetime exercise, but AEW crews are the wary, ever alert men who's nerves are taut for the whole duration of every mission they fly. This is their personal passport to survival, and they are the safety net of the fighting force which they support.

If the last chip is ever down, and an AEW is directly threatened with attack, it is desperate. An AEW aircraft is too vital an organ for military commanders to allocate a recognizable probability of loss. If an AEW aircraft is defeated, the information starvation which would result could

In 1982, when RAF Nimrods were patrolling in the South Atlantic, they encountered Argentine Air Force Boeing 707s on several occasions, and were soon carrying AIM-9 Sidewinder AAMs. It is a safe bet that this installation was a contingency which the RAF had on the shelf, and would have preferred not to reveal until a much later date. This is an MR.2P

be as serious a loss as having a vital artery severed in the human life-support system. In warfare information is like blood, and anaemia could be fatal. One can be sure that every fighter within range which can be used to protect a threatened AEW type will be allocated that task. To some extent, the forces' commander might have to forfeit a temporary set-back through the removal of cover over his ground forces or ships to ensure the long-term survival of this important member of the work force. It would only be at a time such as this, when it would be literally fighting for its own life and those of others over which it casts a friendly eye, that an AEW would ever fire any armament.

It should be clear by now that an AEW fleet cannot operate autonomously. Plans to use AEW types cannot be set in motion without considerable prior consultation about the way that AEW survivability will be ensured. The US, so far the world's only exporter of AEW types, has never yet entered an agreement to sell AEWs without having simultaneously, or previously, established a strong fighter-based defence umbrella over the country in question. A market researcher who might believe that he can identify piecemeal markets for an AEW type, here, there and everywhere, is not aware of the operational consequences of an AEW purchase.

This chapter has tried to show how far an AEW commander will go in preserving his stock of infrared missiles, flares, chaff or whatever until

US Navy operations with the unarmed E-2C Hawkeye involve protection from the Grumman F-14 Tomcat, which has one of the longest-range air-to-air attack systems in the world

Peacetime operations are always likely to be conducted with 'clean' aircraft. Carrying weapons aloft on surveillance aircraft, within national airspace, can be a political embarrassment

the last possible moment. If such devices need to be used once, a full-scale inquiry can be expected immediately, and the crew involved would have to be extremely grateful if they survived. If it happened more than once there would be good reason for believing that something was wrong with the tactics employed. AEW types are not warplanes in the sense that they should never be in pitched battles.

Nevertheless, AEWs will be attacked in real warfare conditions, even though the only way to do it, except for a lucky break, is to confuse the aircraft with so many targets that it cannot cope with the task of sifting the wheat from the chaff (no pun intended!). The solution to this sort of dilemma is in providing for the continual expansion of the technology backing-up the sensors on-board each aircraft, and refining the characteristics of the aircraft's sensors. Bigger and faster central computers and sensor processors, and periodic software up-date programmes, are certain to be in the nature of natural developments in AEW aircraft. Changes such as revised antenna geometry or additional sensor capability is often more difficult to incorporate, but experience shows that as soon as it is necessary, it is incorporated.

In the end, the survivability of an AEW type, and in turn all that it protects, is a responsibility which lays very firmly with the aircraft's crew. From the day he begins training to the instant he relinquishes his last patrol, any AEW crewman, whether a pilot, radar operator, communications controller or an airborne technician, knows that he is just as responsible for his own survival as any crewman charged with operating a weapon-laden aircraft in an attack or fighter squadron, though inevitably an AEW crewman's job is that little bit less glamorous.

Chapter 12
AEW Operators

Those countries who have developed or bought AEW aircraft must surely have had good reason to be convinced that they needed them, for they are an expensive type to acquire and operate. A review of where AEW are found, and what they are doing, reveals a lot of the underlying operational factors, and political innuendos which can interfere with their use.

First, the US armed forces. The US Navy has been the most prolific AEW aircraft operator, and it had around a hundred E-2B and E-2C Hawkeyes in service in the early 1980s. It had been planned that this fleet should stabilise at 84 examples of the E-2C around 1985, but an increase to over 100 is now acknowledged. Aircraft are based at west coast and east coast Naval Air Stations, where they can provide surveillance over strategic harbours and their approaches. These spells on land tend to be used to train crews before their first tour of duty at sea with carriers of the US Navy fleet. Most American carriers have four E-2Cs on-board at any one time, and can have 24-hour cover, albeit a trial for E-2C aircrew and ground crews to provide so much service, for limited periods.

Land-based activity is concentrated at Naval Air Station Norfolk, Virginia, on the US east coast, and Naval Station Miramir, California, on the west coast. These are by no means exclusive land haunts of E-2Cs, but they tend to be transitory visitors to other stations.

Virtually all operational US Navy aircraft carriers operate with a detatchment of four E-2Cs on board. These include the nuclear-powered Nimitz-class vessels *Nimitz*, *Dwight D Eisenhower*, *Carl Vinson* and *Theodore Roosevelt* (in construction) plus the sole example of the *Enterprise* class. There are also *Kitty Hawk*, *Constellation*, *America* and *John F. Kennedy* turbine powered carriers—variously classed as John F. Kennedy or Kitty Hawk class vessels—and The Forrestal-class examples, *Forrestal*, *Saratoga*, *Ranger* and *Independence*. *Midway* and *Coral Sea* can also accommodate a detachment of E-2Cs and the smaller vessels, *Lexington*, *Bon Homme Richard*, *Oriskany* and *Shangrila* are potential

E-2C carriers. The *Bennington* and *Hornet* are laid-up, and although small vessels they would still probably carry E-2Cs if recalled to active duty.

The US Air Force used to have two Airborne Early Warning and Control Wings. The 551st Wing was based at Otis, Massachusetts, and 552nd Wing at MacClellan AFB, California. They were equipped with EC-121s and in operations throughout the 1950s and 1960s they introduced the concept of mobile long-range

These 11 US Navy/Grumman E-2C Hawkeyes were flying from NAS Miramar in California. With production running at six per year, this represents almost two year's procurement of the type

AEW operations. The 551st Wing was disbanded when Norad reached full operational capability and thereafter the 552nd Wing operated in South-East Asia, the Caribbean and Iceland. While supporting US aircraft on operations in South-East Asia, between April 1965 and August 1973, the 552nd Wing logged 98,777 hours in 13,931 sorties. Throughout this period aircraft were based at Tan Son Nut AB, Saigon, and Thai bases at Uban, Udorn and Korat. From patrol patterns over the Gulf of Tonkin the AEW types provided radar monitoring of operations over North Vietnam and Laos, and, to some extent, were able to warn of low-level penetrations from these regions by aggressors.

Operations in the Caribbean and from Iceland were less hectic, but nevertheless contributed significantly to US continental defence and ocean surveillance. The last EC-121 operation from Keflavik, in Iceland, was in 1976, after which a few examples of the type were operated in the US by 79R AEW&C squadron until their eventual retirement in October 1978.

In 1977 the whole of the 552nd Wing was moved to Tinker AFB, Oklahoma, and it prepared to receive the Boeing E-3 Sentry. From this relatively central base the new aircraft can fly to sensitive border areas around the North American mainland, and is able to provide, for the first time, continuous monitoring of overland low-level traffic.

Within a year of service entry in late 1977 the Boeing E-3 revived 552nd tradition by beginning detachments at other bases. Keflavik saw its first jet AEW type in October 1978, and in the following summer the first of what would be annual 150-day detachments to Kadena on Okinawa Island was operated. This was part of a build-up to full-time operations from Kadena in 1983 with four aircraft.

Initial US Air Force procurement plans had been based on the purchase of 34 Boeing E-3s, but with so many global commitments an extra request for 12 further aircraft in late-1982 was inevitable. All the aircraft should be based at Tinker, making it the busiest AEW base in the world, although as permanent detachments of four aircraft each to Keflavik and Kadena are proposed the US Naval Air Stations at Norfolk and Miramar might challenge this claim.

The extra aircraft will also be necessary if the US is to maintain a growing habit. Whenever political activities have threatened friendly nations, the US Air Force has set a precedent for sending AEW aircraft. They can provide surveillance which dramatically improves the capability of the nation's own air force and they can be a very potent stabilizing influence in many politically volatile areas of the world.

Acknowledged surveillance activities in this line have included a rapid deployment of two Boeing E-3s from Okinawa to Riyadh in Saudi Arabia on March 10, 1979. The aircraft monitored an invasion into the Yemen Arab Republic by forces of the Peoples Democratic Republic of Yemen. In mid-December of the same year an E-3 was operated in Egypt, providing air control in Egyptian air force exercises, and although this aircraft returned to the US promptly, within a few weeks two more E-3s flew into Cairo and from there operated along the Gulf region to monitor Soviet activities around Afghanistan.

The most significant Middle East deployment was in September 1980 when Saudi Arabia became host for four aircraft, and which were to be based at Riyadh until at least 1985. The four E-3s provided surveillance after a direct request from the Saudis. This arose from fears that Iran would rout Iraqi forces and try to drive through to the Gulf area. America planned to leave the detachment at Riyadh until such time as the Saudis acquired their own fleet of E-3As, which was the subject of an agreement spelled out in more detail later in this chapter.

In December 1980 four E-3s were also sent to Ramstein in West Germany to monitor Soviet air force movements around Poland at a time when there was considerable political friction in that nation. At least two further detachments, each comprising two aircraft were sent later to Egypt and South Korea, following the assassination of Presidents in both nations. On almost all the above deployments the Boeing E-3A used its air-to-air refuelling capability to good effect, and tended to fly direct to destinations with US Air Force tanker support from overseas sites. In the Korean deployment the aircraft made 14-hour flights, which were not records by any means, and arrived at their destination within 24 hours of mobilization. Within a further 12-hours routine patrols were being operated.

The only occasion when the US has acknowledged that it did not respond to a request for AEW assistance was when Britain asked for E-3 coverage over portions of the South Atlantic during its Falkland Islands Campaign in early-1982. This was refused because the aircraft would have been part of an active battle fleet, and the British could not guarantee continuous fighter support. Other refusals may have been issued, but none has received public attention.

British AEW operations started with the deployments described in Chapter 6, of Douglas Skyraider and Fairey Gannet AEW.3 types on Royal Navy aircraft-carriers. The latter type replaced the Skyraider between 1960–62, and was not withdrawn until HMS *Ark Royal* was taken out of service in 1978. Land-based Shackleton AEW.2 operations, conducted by No. 8 Squadron, Royal Air Force, from Kinloss in Scotland started initially with 12 aircraft in 1972 but from 1981 used only six examples, and all were to be superseded by the Nimrod AEW.3 in 1985. The

TOP US Air Force/Boeing E-3 Sentry fleet stands at readiness on Tinker AFB, Oklahoma, where the 552nd Airborne Warning and Control wing is based

US Air Force crews in their first few years of E-3 operations became used to being sent on quick-reaction surveillance duties throughout the world

RAF has decided to base its 11 British Aerospace Nimrod AEW.3s at Waddington, in Lincolnshire, and transferred personnel to the base in early-1983. From here aircraft can reach patrol areas over the North Sea within about 40 minutes, or be over the North Atlantic region in two hours or less. An hour can be lopped off the transit time to North Atlantic stations by using bases such as Kinloss and St Mawgan. These are existing Nimrod MR.2 bases which could accommodate the new type on a temporary basis without much disruption of existing operations. All Shackleton AEW.2 operations were to be wound down once the Nimrod AEW.3 appeared, and the last operation by this venerable type will represent the end of a 30 odd-year career by the type.

To tell the tale of Britain's other AEW deployment reveals the last AEW type to be introduced in the book, and a bizarre tale of complacency and fate that was responsible for much attention in the late-1982 period. It draws attention to a dilemma that was suffered by the Royal Navy, and which has implications for other naval forces all over the world. The tale is bizarre because it starts off so promisingly, then sinks to a terrifying antithesis, which was only remedied after combat losses.

The Royal Navy had not only been an avid AEW user in the period from 1955 to 1978, during which time aircraft were flown from carriers, but from 1963 it had taken the front-role in AEW design and development in Britain, its work on the P.139 and HS.125-conversion projects having laid foundations for the RAF's land-based AEW Nimrod fleet.

Royal Navy funding, not just of AEW, was decimated by various political manoeuvres in the late-1960s however, and it took a lot of effort, plus tactful use of charisma by various Admirals, before the Navy was authorized to purchase a 'through-deck' cruiser. The aim was to operate Harriers from this flat-topped cruiser which, in due course, was admitted to being an aircraft carrier in all but name. Pathetically, this was necessary to save the embarrassment of politicians who had vowed never to see again an aircraft-carrier in service with the Royal Navy.

Even so, the new ships, and a special-version of Harrier (renamed Sea Harrier), soaked up all the available funding. Something was better than nothing, but the lack of AEW capability on the new ships was worrisome to the astute. In the way that they had had to become accustomed, the Navy Staff kept living on funds that they knew would support only the minimum necessary, and as a direct result shipborne AEW had to be rele-

LEFT AEW Nimrod is the most recent of all Western AEW types to enter service. All 11 aircraft are based at Waddington in Lincolnshire and will operate UK defensive patrols with Tornado F.2 fighters on call to intercept intruders at long range

TOP, ABOVE Royal Navy/Westland AEW Sea King was developed in the wake of several ship losses to sea-skimming missiles in the South Atlantic during 1982. The radome is being swivelled aft before landing. AEW Sea King has a modified EMI Searchwater radar antenna in the radome, and can provide all-round surveillance. Even so, it is not as good a system as the Royal Navy deserves, and was prepared to buy as long ago as 1966

gated to a low level of priority. No AEW aircraft was operated on the new British carrier fleet.

The fact that the subject had been viewed seriously, and at the right time, is not in any doubt however. No sooner had P.139 been washed away by political waves than designs were prepared showing the installation of AEW radar in Sea King helicopters. The drawings exist in filing cabinets throughout the industry, bearing dates in 1966, maybe even earlier, and sadly that is where British naval AEW lanquished for almost a decade and a half. Several interim proposals were made, including one which suggested use of a modified EMI Searchwater radar in a retractable radome on Sea King helicopters, which was submitted in 1981. Like all previous proposals this was rejected.

On May 4, 1982, during the Falklands campaign, a single Exocet missile launched from a low-flying Super Etendard strike aircraft operated by the Argentine Navy struck and sunk HMS *Sheffield*, north-west of the Falkland Islands. This was a major victory for the Argentine Navy, and they repeated this success subse-quently, with both the sea-skimming Exocet against vessels at sea, and with conventional bombs lofted onto ships in coastal waters and at anchor. The attacks, the loss of human life, and the publicity which resulted, achieved more in a few days than a hundred committees had been able to do in a decade and a half. Only 14 weeks after that first Exocet had hammered home the fact that there was a big hole in the Royal Navy's defences, an AEW type was not only designed, but it was developed, built, commissioned and sent-off to operate in the South Atlantic. This was an AEW Sea King which is in essence a watered-down version of what had been proposed about 16 years earlier, and identical to the 1981 proposal.

It is ironic that the Royal Navy, after having been such a leading supporter of AEW development, should have had to suffer so ignominiously for the lack of the same. There are many in the Navy who would have said more, and more vitriolically, than is said here, and undoubtedly if the Treasury constraints on AEW/Navy expenditure had an easily isolated root, blood would have been spilt behind the scenes in 1982. As it was, the AEW Sea King became available, and it became inconceivable that the Royal Navy would ever again be forced to operate at sea without AEW cover.

AEW Sea King is not sophisticated, and the British authorities have discouraged attention to the detail of the project. Nevertheless, it is a grand testimony to what can be achieved quickly, and it should be a starting point for things better in the future.

The AEW Sea King was developed jointly by Westland and Thorn-EMI, and the whole programme took only 11 weeks from go-ahead to commissioning date. The latter company took an example of its Searchwater radar, the main airborne sensor in the Nimrod MR.2 anti-submarine fleet, and incorporated changes to its clutter-rejection system that made it suitable for detecting low-level targets. The basic Searchwater is optimized for surface-target detection, and although its performance figures are classified it is generally acknowledged to be able to distinguish a snorkel from sea clutter at up to 10 nm. If this is the case it should have no difficulty in detecting a sea-skimming anti-ship missile at 20 nm., which is about the maximum operating range of most types. An aircraft carrying such weapons would probably be detectable at up to twice this distance.

The radar is mounted in a pressurized radome which swivels from a horizontal position after

Behind the scenes, there is a lot of activity that keeps AEW crews in top condition. This flight simulator is at Tinker AFB and was supplied to the US Air Force by British manufacturer Rediffusion. The company would undoubtedly have supplied an example to Nato too, had Britain not gone alone with the AEW Nimrod programme

take-off until it is vertical and has an uninterrupted view in all-directions beneath the helicopter. Communications, initially at least, were not
sophisticated, and radar operator warnings
would probably be sent by secure voice
radio-link.

Britain is in an enviable situation in one respect. It has a system born out of bitter experience, and used operationally, and its experience
has shown other navies how vulnerable their
ships must be too. This applies not just to aircraft
carriers, but to any high-value vessel which will
be a prime target in a time of hostilities. With
an already sizeable and expanding armoury of
anti-ship missiles in service worldwide the threat
to all navies is considerable, and the market for
a low-cost AEW type such as Sea King may be
ready for exploitation.

Soviet AEW operations, or at least what little
is known about them, are described in the chapter
devoted to the Tupolev Tu-126 Moss. Only a few
examples of this land-based aircraft are known

The Nato purchase of 18 Boeing E-3 Sentrys will probably
be the biggest single export order ever awarded to an AEW
manufacturer. It was won after half a decade of regrettable
and unnecessary polititical bickering between European
Nato nations

to have been in service, and the liklihood of a new
type coming along has been forecast for several
years. Little is ever said however about the Soviet
Navy's views on AEW operations, and with its
own equivalent of Britain's through-deck
cruiser—ie; an aircraft-carrier in all but name,
although this time so that it can sail through the
Bosphorus into the Mediterranean without
breaching a paper treaty that is as good as worth-
less—there is clearly a requirement for it to use
its own seaborne-AEW aircraft. A likely candidate to carry radar to detect anti-ship missiles
would be the Kamov Helix helicopter, which is
roughly equivalent to the western operated Sea
King.

All remaining AEW operators fall into a very
different category to those already described.

None of them has designed or built its own aircraft and systems for this role. They are the operators who have bought in to meet requirements which they cannot meet indigenously, either because of the high-technology involved, or due to their small needs, which might not warrant committing a large proportion of available technical resources. The biggest current user in this category, and likely to remain so because it is an alliance rather than a single nation, is the North Atlantic Treaty Organisation (Nato). At the time, its AEW procurement procedures did a lot to bring AEW aircraft to the attention of the public, and it commanded headlines for several years.

As early as 1974 Nato had decided that the Boeing E-3A Sentry, with modifications which had been discussed with Washington officials, would be suitable for operations in Western Europe, where there was a pressing requirement for an AEW type to monitor the land and sea borders with Eastern Bloc countries. All the formal procedures had been gone through by January 1976 and the US DoD provided a quote to Nato for a 32-aircraft fleet. The price would be $2100 million basic, plus $150 million for ESM equipment and $300 million for further enhancements. The latter included maritime-surveillance radar capability, greater auto-tracking capability, secure data-link, frequency-agility features and doubled central computer capacity. The deal offered a lot of European industrial offset which added 10 per cent to the total price, bringing the total purchase price to around $2700 million. Of this, about 25 per cent would be produced in Nato countries other than the US.

The American incentives were very appealing, and too appealing to some US politicians who questioned how Nato could be offered 32 aircraft at a basic price of $2100 million, whereas the US Air Force was paying $3500 million for 34 aircraft. A protracted argument ensured about what is basic and what is not, and the conclusion in all respects was that the USAF wasn't robbed, and also that Nato probably couldn't find a better deal anywhere.

In June 1976, when everything looked right, internal procrastinations forced Nato to delay making any decision on procurement. The purchase could only continue however if the Nato Awacs Project Office in The Hague remained active. To assure its continuation the US made available $6 million, Britain and West Germany contributed $4 million each, and the rest of Nato sank in $2 million. This was sufficient to keep the Office available for only six more months, and by now Britain, who was already spending almost

Nato's first Boeing E-3 was photographed by a Boeing cameraman as it cruised over the ash-lined caldera of Mount St. Helens volcano, only a hundred miles or so south of Boeing's Renton factory

$2 million per month on an indigenous AEW programme, was saying publicly that it was fed up with Nato indecisiveness.

There was a determined attempt in late-1976 to get France to join a Nato purchase, by offering CFM-56 engines. CFM International, the engine manufacturer, claimed a 16 per cent on-station time advantage and that the bigger turbofan could cope with the extraordinary avionics power demands better than the Pratt & Whitney TF-33-100A engines. Pratt & Whitney countered the aggressive campaign by citing Nato

Awacs Project Office assessments which it said showed a $213.9 million life-cycle saving if the existing engine was retained. A 100 per cent European-build offset on the TF-33 engine was offered too.

Around late 1976 Boeing Aerospace also awarded a formal $1.8 million development contract to Westinghouse to incorporate maritime-surveillance capability in future examples of the radar. Everything seemed to be reaching top gear, and optimism rose again when during two meetings of senior Nato financial controllers in

Brussels, on January 11/12 and 19/20, 1977, plans which outlined the mechanics of a $2400 million purchase were agreed. The latter covered 27 aircraft, and all expenditure up to 1985. The plan assumed that Britain and the US would shoulder the majority of costs up to 1979, after which time West Germany would begin to absorb the largest proportion, and by 1982 this would be roughly equalled, after a period of growing contributions, by Canada. Nato Assistant Secretary-General DR Laberge announced the following breakdown of costs;

US	$680 million
West Germany	$630 million
UK	$432 million
Canada	$190 million
France	not in agreement as CFM-56 proposal not accepted
Italy	less than $100 million
Belgium	$70–50 million
The Netherlands	$70–50 million
Denmark	$48 million
Turkey	$20 million
Portugal	$7 million
Greece	$6 million (uncertain)
Luxembourg	$2 million
Iceland	not expected to contribute

Contributions in each financial year were to total as follows;

1977	$125–130 million
1978	$400 million
1979	$400 million
1980	$400 million
1981	$350 million
1982	$350 million
1983	$275 million
1984	$110 million
1985	$10 million

The optimism was soon shattered however. After the financial controllers the politicians took over, and they made as big a mountain as has ever been made out of a molehill. First, the West German Government attacked the US bitterly for breaking off agreements to develop a common Main Battle Tank, and virtually threatened to withdraw from the E-3A purchase agreement. Secondly, the small Nato nations asked the four major partners to increase their contributions by five per cent. The UK declined to exceed $450 million, saying that this was the ceiling it put on development of its own AEW Nimrod programme.

In other words, by the time that Nato defence ministers met on February 17 there was bedlam. Only 6 of the 12 nations involved had agreed to foot their proportions of the bill. These were the US, West Germany, UK (subject to $450 million ceiling), Norway, Canada and Luxembourg. Portugal emphatically denied that it would contribute even $7 million, Italy pleaded poverty and

Boeing, more than any other aircraft manufacturer, knows how to dress a hangar for an aircraft roll-out. The British flag is not amongst those of other Nato nations after she had decided to develop an independent AEW fleet

A multi-national Nato crew readies an E-3 for a patrol.
Training was conducted with the US Air Force prior to
aircraft reaching Europe

asked for a drastic cut of its $100 million portion, and Belgium, apparently completely ignorant about what an AEW fleet represented, said it would contribute its share only if it was used to upgrade existing ground-based surveillance radar stations in the country.

Under the circumstances, Nato ministers did well to get agreement to meet again only a month later, by which time they hoped to have found a way of reducing the overall bill by $300 million. However, things didn't run so true to the plans, and the March meeting was cancelled.

A couple of weeks later Britain pulled out. It could no longer afford to support its own project and subsidize Nato vacillations. Shortly before AEW Nimrod was launched the UK claimed that 7000 jobs would be created at home by choosing the homespun product, compared to only 450 if the Boeing E-3A was purchased. The claim was that either option amounted to the same cost to the British taxpayer.

Boeing was determined to get across in the UK their belief that the UK employment claims were wrong, and three days after the above figures had been released the American firm had a team in

Britain to brief journalists, and no doubt Whitehall too, on their point of view. They saw approaching 1000 jobs in the UK (the breakdown was 520 at BAC/HSA, 251 at Shorts, 225 at Marconi-Elliott and 63 at Redifon Simulation), plus at least 2000 on a maintenance base which would be in the UK.

Britain ignored the claims and although through going alone it put the whole Nato AEW purchase programme back in the melting pot, it did bring a lot of the bickering factions in Nato to their senses. It had one other very significant effect too, as it now released for redistribution in other Nato nations the jobs which would have been in Britain's contribution to the Nato project. To the West German's, who have difficult job settling their balance of payments with the US at the best of times, this was particularly welcome. An ironic twist for one UK firm was that Redifon, who had worked hard to win the contract to supply an E-3A flight simulator to the

US Air Force, and had had the satisfaction of seeing the equipment commissioned on schedule at Tinker in September 1976, now lost the chance of building a second unit for Nato.

In October 1977 a US Air Force E-3 was deployed to Ramstein, in West Germany. Coincidentally, Nato ministers were meeting at the time to review procurement plans and delegates for once could see the hardware that they were intending to buy. By now however Nato's requirement had dropped to 18 aircraft, and the US authorities quoted $1700 million for the fleet. It was agreed that they could be based in West Germany, although stipulated that the base should be as far west as possible. Subsidiary bases in Norway, Italy and Turkey were proposed simultaneously.

The next meeting of Nato finance ministers which specifically considered the E-3A purchase was in February 1978, and they discovered that the 18 aircraft now commanded a $2000 million price tag. This was found to be generally acceptable however, and a final decision by defence ministers was slated for May, with an intention to get every nation to sign the contract for aircraft by October of the same year. If this timetable was achieved Nato felt confident of seeing its first E-3A in service by 1982, which was coincident with UK plans. The purchase agreement now considered that Boeing would install only the radar and navigation equipment before aircraft left Seattle, and the rest of the equipment would be fitted in Europe.

The defence ministers managed to agree to the purchase in May 1978, as scheduled. They were to buy 18 aircraft at a total price of $1900 million, and the main base in Europe was to be Geilenkirchen. Each nation's bill over five years worked out approximately thus:

US	$760 million	40%
West Germany	$570 million	30%
Canada	$190 million	10%
Italy	$95 million	5%
Belgium	$67 million	3.5%
Denmark	$38 million	2%
Norway	$38 million	2%
Turkey	$19–38 million	1–2%
Luxembourg	$19 million	1%
Portugal	around	1%
Greece	around	1%

The signatures collected at the time were for an interim purchase agreement, and the final contract took three years to complete. On 15 May 1981 Belgium, initially skeptical about the whole programme, signed its commitment, claiming that to balance its defence expenditure it was deferring the purchase of 48 combat helicopters, and cutting back on F-16 development. It was the final dissenting word about the whole deal, and the end of a political saga that had dragged on for almost five years.

As expected West Germany got a large proportion of the technical offset. SEL manufactured much of the display and communications equipment, AEG-Telefunken contributed also to the communications equipment, and the radar. MTU produced a large proportion of engine parts, and ESG became involved in development of the system software for the new central computer. Canadian firms did well too, Fleet Industries getting the engine nacelle manufacturing contract, and CAE was selected to supply the flight simulator which Britain had otherwise seemed certain to build.

Maritime-surveillance capability, the crucial new feature of the radar for Nato operations, was tested by Westinghouse in 1979, and entered flight test in mid-1980. By early 1982 all aircraft, USAF production included, had this feature incorporated.

Nato crewmen began training at Tinker with the USAF 552nd Airborne and Warning Control Wing in July 1980, on courses that lasted up to 55 weeks, and no fewer than 370 crewmen had been trained by autumn 1982. The first Nato E-3A was rolled-out at Boeing Field on 27 January 1981, having flown there, without its rotodome, from the manufacturing plant a few miles away at Renton, on 18 December 1980. This aircraft was handed over to Dornier at Oberpfaffenhofen, near Munich, on 31 March 1981, where installation of the internal systems was to be conducted. This represented the beginning of a very substantial contract for West Germany as it covered all 18 aircraft, and was expected to lead to the award of the in-service maintenance contract to Dornier also.

On 22 January 1982 the first Nato E-3A was handed over to US Major General Leighton Palmerton, Nato AEW Force Commander, and later was delivered to Geilenkirchen. The delivery schedule called for nine aircraft to be in service by December 1983, and for the last aircraft to reach the fleet in January 1985. By late 1983 four forward operating bases were to be commissioned too, at Trapani (Sicily), Preveza (Greece), Konya (Turkey) and Oerland (Norway). The operating schedule called for 12 aircraft to be at Geilenkirchen at all times, and for each aircraft to fly, on average, 65 hours per month. The main base will eventually employ 2462 service personnel.

All 41 radar stations in the Nadge radar chain, which extends from Norway to Turkey, had to be modified to interface with the E-3A, and this effort got underway in September 1982 when Visselhoevede in West Germany and Skrydstrup in Denmark were modified. The cost of this programme is revealed in the breakdown below. It was released in early 1982, but quoted prices in mid-1977 dollars:

18 × E-3A aircraft	$1524 million
Modernization of Nadge site	$181 million
Dornier (install & check-out)	$107 million
Main base facilities	$52 million
Forward operating bases	$18 million
Unspecified	$44 million
TOTAL	$1826 million

The Nato contract was undoubtedly the biggest AEW export deal ever likely to be signed, and involving a dozen or so nations it was bound to be protracted, and highly political. However, in late-1981, and in connection with a much smaller E-3A sales deal, political temperatures almost reached boiling point again. This time the strife was in the US, and it was all because of a purchase request from Saudi Arabia.

It all started in April 1981 when President Reagan approved the sale of $5000 million-worth of aircraft and equipment to Saudi Arabia. The deal included 62 McDonnell Douglas F-15s, six Boeing 707 tankers (called KC-707s, to differentiate them from the KC-135, which was out of production) and five Boeing E-3A Sentry AEW aircraft. The latter fleet was selected by Saudi Arabia over an alternative offer of 11 Grumman E-2C Hawkeyes.

The deal was bound to be unpopular in the US House of Representatives, where there was a very strong pro-Israeli lobby, and their rumblings were distinct from the moment Reagan had made

his announcement. Gradually the grand masters in the political arena got hold of the undercurrents and seemed for awhile likely to turn them into a rip-tide. Their arguments were not only about US support for Israel, but also about whether US airmen would be liable to crew the aircraft during times of hostilities, and especially about whether equipment was liable to fall into Soviet hands.

The latter fear was a reaction after Iran had signed a purchase agreement for seven E-3As in July 1977, and with full US Government approval. Iranian Deputy Minister of War General Hassen Toufanian made a formal statement at the time, and a letter of intent was placed in April 1978, against which the US had planned deliveries between 1981–1983. All that changed, literally overnight, when the Ayatollah Khomeini overthrew the Shah of Iran in February 1979. The E-3A never went to Iran therefore, but the vast numbers of F-14 Tomcat fighters and their highly capable Phoenix missiles which had been delivered already became totally inaccessible.

Although the radical Islam ruler in Iran was no friend of communism, the proximity of the Soviet border to many F-14 bases in Iran was felt at the time to represent the most serious technical loss to the US that had ever happened.

Reagan's controversial offer to the Saudis had to be put before both houses in the US Congress, the House of Representatives and the Senate. It had to be rejected by both for the deal to be called off, but the opposition was clearly going to be formidable. The bill containing the sales agreement was tabled late in September 1981, and it had to be accepted or rejected within 30 days.

The US Administration immediately organized briefings for politicians and defence officials. These were designed to allay fears about the technology involved in the deal, and the statistics which were produced should not have surprised anyone, but as the briefings proceeded and political tempers rose it became clear that many US politicians had previously believed erroneous claims that these 'eye in the sky' aircraft could see everything as clearly as a binocular-equipped observer on a gin clear day. The true limitations of AEW radars were interpreted by opponents to the deal as a deliberate smokescreen by the Administration. Radar detection range was quoted to be 175 nm against a small fighter, and 240 nm against a medium-sized target. Ground detail and aircraft flying at less than 80 knots were invisible. The briefings pointed out that US Air Force and Nato-operated E-3s could achieve better target-detection performance.

In the second week of October the House of Representatives rejected the sale by an overwhelming 301 to 111 vote decision. The crucial Senate debate was set for 26 October, and running up to that date US television networks ran an endless number of programmes forecasting the Senate vote, and explaining at length the Boeing E-3A's performance to the American public. Reagan conducted a campaign amongst the Senators which included breakfast telephone conversations on the day of the vote, and he got what we wanted by the slimmest of majorities: 52 to 48 votes.

AEW deliveries to the Royal Saudi Air Force were to take place between 1983 and 1985. Plans called for all the fleet of five aircraft to be at Riyadh until 1986, then to move 60 nm southeast to a new base at Al-Kharj. US crews will take part in operations, but sufficient Saudi crewmen should be available for all US crews to be withdrawn by 1990. Saudi will use the aircraft to pa-

The first Nato-operated E-3 arrives at its home base, at Geilenkirchen, in West Germany

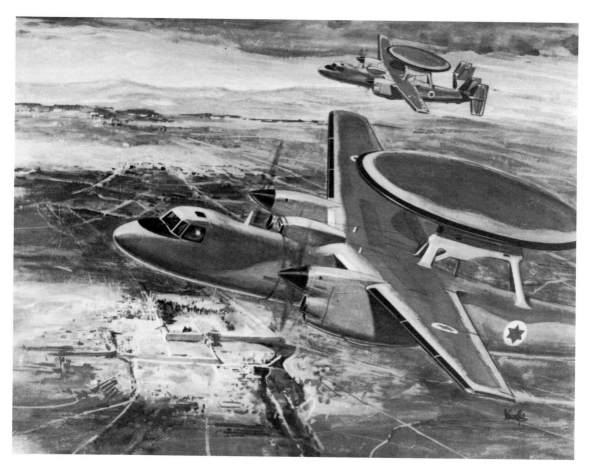

trol along the Gulf States, where US Air Force E-3s on detachment have operated since 1981, and to monitor air movements across neighbouring areas to the north.

Four further US AEW export deals have been concluded without the trauma of the Nato and Saudi E-3A agreements. All of the deals involve the Grumman E-2C Hawkeye.

Four E-2C Hawkeyes have served in Israel since about 1976. Israel is the only nation to have used AEW in anger, both to counter incoming raids and to co-ordinate the movement of its own aircraft at long-ranges. Israeli tactics in connection with raids into Syria, the Lebanon and Iraq have been described as brilliant by many well-recognized military leaders. About all that Israel has acknowledged openly however is the claim that Syrian-operated MiGs can be detected as they take off from bases near to Damascus is, in essence, true. With so much early-warning capability the Israelis can often tailor the defensive tactics that they use to protect their own forces very rapidly, and without having to mount large safeguard operations.

In operations against surface-to-air missile (SAM) sites in the Bekaa Valley (these were Syr-

Israel is the world's most discrete AEW operator, with four Grumman E-2C Hawkeyes monitoring the volatile borders of the Middle East, and co-ordinating many Israeli Air Force offensives. Authentic data of Israel's experience with Hawkeye is hard to find. One has to presume it is an exceedingly valuable aircraft

ian-operated batteries in the Lebanon) during 1982 it has been claimed that remotely-piloted vehicles were steered over the area, equipped to look to electronic detection equipment like Israeli fighters. When SAM acquisition radars were detected by E-2Cs patrolling off the coast of Lebanon, fighters which were just out of Syrian radar coverage were vectored in rapidly, at low-level. With anti-radiation missiles they destroyed the radars immediately, thus neutralizing SAM defences in the area. This sort of AEW experience is unique, and it is a pity that more cannot be said, although Israel's military logic in hiding from the discussion of all such rumours is quite understandable. A Grumman brochure captures Israel's reticence most eloquently by saying 'Israel has requested that Grumman not discuss delivery and operational plans.' In a nutshell; it's a very effective aircraft.

The most recent of E-2C deliveries began on

18 May 1982 when the Japanese Air Self Defence Force took delivery of its first Grumman E-2C Hawkeye at Grumman's Bethpage factory. Eight E-2Cs are to be delivered to Japan according to funding arrangements concluded at the time this was written, but it was anticipated that several more would be added, at the rate of one or two aircraft per year until at least 15 E-2Cs are in service in Japan.

Last of the initial batch of eight aircraft was due to be in Japanese service by late-1983, and the Hawkeye squadron will be based at Misawa in the north of the Japanese islands. The aircraft will be used primarily to monitor Soviet shipping and air activities in the Northwest Pacific, and as it is mainly an overwater operation in an island-dotted region the E-2C should be especially suited to Japanese requirement.

Egypt and Singapore were confirmed as the latest overseas purchasers of the E-2C in early-1983, and are due to receive aircraft from 1985.

One problem with looking at the AEW market in detail is that in the current climate, when nations are deliberating how to tighten their defences and simultaneously not appear to be too aggressive, AEW is becoming a favourite point

Japan began to take delivery of Grumman E-2C Hawkeyes in 1982, and will operate at least eight, but probably as many more as the country can afford, to monitor shipping and low-flying aircraft activities in the North West Pacific region

of discussion, provided the operational requirements can be met cost-effectively. It is quite likely that France will have decided to purchase AEW types before this book is published, and had seen the E-2C and E-3 at first hand at the time of writing. Rumblings of favour for the E-2C have been heard, and the differentiating factor has always been quoted to be price. The US and Boeing in particular are keen to get France involved in E-3A operations, to standardize AEW operations in Europe, but the way to success will not be easy as there are few nations who can be tempted to a more expensive choice just to suit their neighbours.

Australia has always been a potential AEW customer, but costs always seem to swamp procurement off the nation's small budget. Whether UK experience post-Falkland will influence this nation, and others with vulnerable navies, remains to be seen.

Chapter 13
AEW in the Future

Being convinced that what is fashionable today will still be the height of fashion tomorrow has trapped many unsuspecting forecaster, and with AEW operations having blossomed out of small beginnings into big business during the 1970s, there is the temptation to believe that the AEW industry, once started, will grow forever. This isn't true, and this book has said enough already about the enormous costs involved in AEW operations to have shown that not everyone can look forward to having rows and rows of AEW aircraft on their airfields in the future. Nevertheless, everyone would like an AEW, so perhaps demand will cause AEW aircraft to change in character, taking on a new appearance.

Throughout this book the AEW story has unfolded as a tale of aircraft developments, with a short airship interlude, driven by advances in radar technology. That technology could be made available more cheaply, and indeed with electronic developments on the course they seem sure to follow this is inevitable, but the overall effect on AEW costs is likely to be insufficient to ever make these types fall into the everyman's category. Sufficient has been said to illustrate that there is more to an AEW than just a collection of computers handling various chores. That is the way they are basically configured, but they will take on new orders of complexity as ways of spoofing existing systems are perfected. Attempts to develop cheaper AEW technologies will be frustrated by the residue of this technology race. The outcome will be that, of those who enter the race, only the rich will be sure of getting richer, and the poor will probably get poorer. Instead of trying to predict how existing AEW techniques will adjust to change it will be worth considering if there is an alternative technology that could upset the evolving marketplace.

An AEW customer is looking for a detection system which will provide him with warning of

Whatever turns future AEW technology takes, there is unlikely to be an aircraft in this category which will eclipse the Grumman E-2 Hawkeye. It was as bold in its day as any space project, and it is by far the most numerous AEW type in service

airborne threats sufficiently far away for tactical action to be taken to neutralize their effectiveness. There are ways in which this can be achieved more effectively than with the current generation of AEW types.

First, raising the AEW platform to a much higher altitude will increase the distance to the radar horizon. The table below shows how much can be gained by taking radar into the upper regions of the atmosphere. Note that 150,000 ft altitude is about 25 nm, and the area covered by surveillance to the horizon is a little over 750,000 sq miles. (cf: 150,000 sq miles for a typical existing system).

AEW height (ft)	Radar horizon (nm)
30,000	219
50,000	283
70,000	335
100,000	400
150,000	490

The difficulty of sifting and analyzing all the information in such an area, which could represent 3,000 or so targets at any instant in time, are less daunting now that the necessary techniques have been proven in existing AEW systems. The predicted rate of evolution of larger memory and higher-speed electronic systems to meet such requirements suggests that suitable units are likely to be available by 1990.

But getting a radar to such altitudes and keeping it there is not necessarily an easy task. There is some prospect of having available balloons with sufficient displacement to take such a payload so far aloft, and as experience with the Goodyear airships proved, plus demonstrations with the Airship Industries AD-500 in Britain at the time of writing, a radar antenna can be enclosed in the vehicle envelope. Such a method of transporting the equipment to altitude would be relatively cheap and effective, especially if the balloon is unmanned, in which case it would use microwave communications to the ground or lower altitude airborne command-post aircraft. Indeed, the prospect is so promising that if the market for such systems was substantial—but unfortunately it isn't because even the superpowers would need very few examples each—a specialized aircraft, which could be envisaged to have many Lockheed U-2 characteristics, would be predictable. The latter can only come about if other roles demanding a similar vehicle emerge, and at the moment that doesn't seem likely. It looks as if the next generation AEW, if different in any way at all from existing types, will

either cruise substantially higher—say between 50,000 and 70,000 ft—or be a remotely-controlled balloon of gigantic dimensions.

A second way of detecting threats at long-ranges does not require getting airborne at all. Again, it is radar engineers who have devised the new way of seeing further. The technique is called over-the-horizon (OTH) radar. OTH radars are already in service, and their operating principles, although complex, are well understood. They operate like conventional radars, emitting pulses at regular intervals and analyzing the responses from targets within the area of coverage. To see beyond where conventional radars cut-off they use high-frequency (HF) radiation. In this context the nomenclature is confusing, as the frequencies used are considerably lower than those commonplace in conventional radars. Current AEW types use radiation between 2 to 4 GHz frequency (15 to 7.5 cm wavelength) and OTH radars use frequencies measurable in kilohertz, which represents wavelengths of many hundreds of metres.

These long-wavelength signals are used because they can be trapped between ionized layers in the upper atmosphere and the earth's surface, and so they bounce around the curvature of the earth. OTH radar operation is not so easy as such a simple description pretends however. The ionized layers move up and down, especially between day and night, and vary in strength, sometimes letting a lot of radiation leak off into space. The propagation and attenuation characteristics of signals are therefore far from simple. Furthermore, because the wavelengths are large the OTH radar antenna, if it is to be efficient, needs to be large too. It tends to be a complex and vulnerable piece of equipment. A direct consequence is that OTH radars have to use enormously-expensive ground-stations, and all those being built currently use phased-array antennas whose phase shifters direct radiation across a limited field-of-view.

Target resolution can be poor, partly because of the long wavelength, and also because long-duration pulses are used to get large amounts of energy out to the ranges of several hundreds of miles, or even in excess of a thousand miles. These drawbacks are being compensated by using pulse-compression techniques and pieces

The US Air Force, by pursuing a lengthy yet methodical development programme, acquired land-based AEW capability much later than the US Navy achieved it at sea. Although large and expensive, the Boeing E-3 Sentry is already in build for overseas customers, and it is the aircraft that has captured most public attention

of even more recent technology. A very severe drawback however is that there is little chance of integrating a passive-detection system with an OTH radar, so methods of target-recognition based on modified radar system operation are having to be considered by researchers currently. Techniques spoken of include varying the radar pulse shape. Instead of using simple pulses which turn on and off abruptly they use pulses that gradually increase in intensive and fall off rapidly, or slowly again (they are called saw-tooth or sine-wave pulses), and it may be that with such radars there will be sufficient difference in the responses generated by different shape targets that some identification is possible. Without this sort of capability, until one had watched the target for a long period, it might not be possible to tell the difference between a warship and a helicopter cruising slowly on anti-submarine duties. Even when these are distinguishable, the radar responses of small and large vessels may not always be unambiguous. OTH radar remains complementary to, rather than challenging, AEW types.

OTH radar can be an excellent long-range sensor which will forewarn AEW aircraft of likely intruders, and therefore reduces the time needed to identify new tracks as they appear over the AEW radar horizon. This process is used in the US where large OTH radars have been installed looking outwards from each seaboard. There may also be a case for using OTH radars as a more independent detection system in countries such as South Africa and Australia, where the direction from which threats are most likely to occur are established, and large areas need to be monitored. At the current time however, any military authority wanting to trust OTH technology without some degree of AEW system to supplement it would be certainly accused of recreating the anomolous situation that characterized Singapore's gun defences.

One other radar development might be significant, and in that it has been recently put into production it could be more influential than either high-altitude AEW or OTH radar. The new system is called synthetic-aperture radar (SAR). A

SAR set looks exactly like a conventional pulse-Doppler radar, but its processor stores the multitude of data accumulated over several scans.

It has been stressed several times before that the bigger a radar antenna, the better is the resolution, or picture quality, obtained. This is achieved artificially in the SAR radar, as the stored data is analyzed by computer to deduce detail equivalent to using an antenna as long as the aircraft flightpath. SAR receivers small enough to fit in existing ground-attack aircraft are already available, and within a few seconds of completing several scans they provide a radar image filled with astonishing detail. Roads, hedges, railways, streets, quaysides, shipping and so on are all visible. Note however that the technique is only really useful when the scene is being viewed from abeam, in other words areas directly ahead or aft cannot be seen clearly, and the radar antenna must not be too low, or tall objects will create unacceptable shadow regions.

In researching this book, on several occasions it was interesting to hear unofficial views from several experts on what they felt were SAR implementations in AEW operations. Unanimously, and surprisingly, they were unimpressed. Their arguments were very sound however.

Although SAR opens the possibility of discovering a lot of ground threat detail, and their are few military services who wouldn't endorse the development of a system that might be able to see missile sites, supply depots and even troop convoys as they happen, an AEW antenna would be operating at very shallow viewing angles in current operations, and would suffer unacceptable degrees of shadowing beyond enemy frontlines. In other words, to see sufficient, the AEW aircraft would have to run the risk of exposing itself to the very threats it was trying to find. An AEW aircraft is too valuable to be used so indiscriminantly, and a far more equitable solution would be to use remotely-piloted vehicles.

As matters stand in respect of all foreseeable sensor and airborne system technology therefore, AEW aircraft are certain of a reasonable lifespan. Unless there is some revolutionary sensor in prospect which the military will keep to itself, in just the way that Britain nurtured long-range radar in the late-1930s, it seems unlikely that AEW importance will diminish at all in the next 15–25 years. There is every reason to expect that most nations with an AEW capability in the 21st century will still be using a form of pulse-Doppler radar, associated with identification systems.

The proportions of simplified and sophisticated types might vary a lot however, depending on political and economic influences, and as not even the experts in these fields can forecast with reasonable certainty it would be unwise to try identifying any trends and to extrapolate them here. The only certainty is that any trend towards making effective AEW types less expensive, if not exactly cheap, will be sure to open a substantial market.

For the romantics, sadly therefore, the world has become a less euphoric place for aviators. Each morning, even in peacetime nowadays, crews are up there, and their task is no less serious than that of the old-time dawn patrol, although they are warmer and more comfortable, enclosed

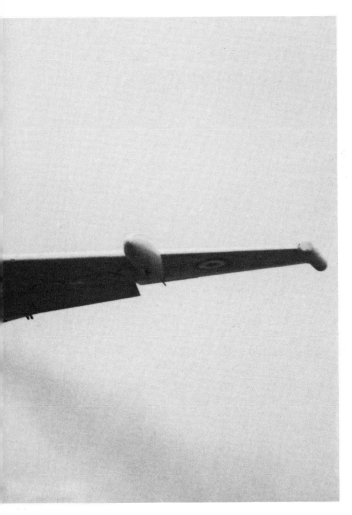

Perhaps wresting from the Grumman E-2 Hawkeye the prize for ugliest duckling, Britain's AEW Nimrod shows that while everyone else is content with a roof-top view from their AEW types, British engineers prefer to mount their look-outs in airborne balconies. This imaginative project is doomed to commercial failure by the British Government's reluctance to re-establish a Nimrod production line

in the pressurized hulls of modern military leviathans.

The pilots will still be able to see the earth from an angle that leaves no one who has seen it in doubt of how beautiful a display nature can provide. Viewed from high altitude dawn can be a moving experience. Stars still shine in an inky-black zenith even after the first brilliant rays of sunlight have lanced across from the horizon, then rapidly they are extinguished. On cloudless mornings moisture in the air many miles below often hangs in the air, curling along coastlines and over shallow, warm seas. It can look beautiful from above but this is the menacing fog that has become all in a day's work for the modern ter-rain-following sniper. It might have deterred raiders a decade or two ago, and it would have grounded a dawn patrol, but now the AEW sits above it all. It operates obediently, forgotten by the majority of the population it protects perhaps, but ensuring that they have the best of modern-day protection. Indeed, AEW is an important modern deterrent. The nations who have invested in them make no mistake about claiming that they believe the world is a more peaceful place with AEW aircraft about.

Although the legends of the dawn patrol have become echoing memories, airborne sentinels must still maintain guard. A US Air Force/Boeing E-3 Sentry pauses to take on fuel during an early morning patrol

Acknowledgements

It is always a pleasure to find helping hands when one comes to compile an untold tale, and but for many good helpers who have sifted through files, dug out forgotten facts, submitted photographs old and new, and any number of unexpected surprises, this book would have never been written. The following organizations deserve special mention: Boeing Aerospace Company, British Aerospace, Civil Aviation Authority, Flight International, General Electric, Grumman Aerospace, Imperial War Museum, Lockheed Corporation, Marconi Avionics, McDonnell Douglas, Ministry of Defence, Pilot Press, Rediffusion Simulation, Royal Air Force, Royal Signals and Radar Establishment, Thorn-EMI, United States Air Force, Westinghouse and Westland Aircraft.

Individuals who have made contributions, large and small, are almost too numerous to mention, but I would like to thank the following in particular: Jock Aytoun, Dick Baird, Clif Bickle, Roy Boot, Don Brannon, Dr John Clarke, John Dailey, Michael Farlam, Jim Grafton, Harry Holmes, Alex Johnson, Dick King, John Kinnear, Kris Lane, Jim Lyons, Bob McCluskey, Geoff Norris, Steve Piercey, Alex Rubach, Jim Robertson, 'Schoney' Schonenberg, Bill Spaniel, Jim Stuart, Karen Stubberfield, Bill Skillman, Barry Wheeler and Gordy Williams. The list is undoubtedly too short, and for omissions I have to include my apologies.

A special mention is deserved for Janet Henty, who converted my rough copy into immaculate shape, and against crippling timescales, for presentation to security and the publisher, and Roger Daniels who has made such good use of photographs and artwork in the layout. With such good help, and against all odds, the pages presented here were duly completed. It remains for me to point out that the opinions expressed are my own.

Abbreviations

ACLS	Automatic carrier landing system
ADC	Air-data computer
ADF	Automatic direction finder
AEW	Airborne early warning
AFB	Air Force Base (USAF)
AFCS	Automatic flight control system
AHRS	Attitude and heading reference system
AI	Airborne interception
Amrics	Auto-management of radio and intercom by computer
AMTI	Airborne moving-target indicator
AOCP	Airborne operational computer program
ARPS	Advanced radar processing system
Awacs	Airborne warning and control system
BAC	British Aircraft corporation
BTH	Beyond-the-horizon
Cains	Carrier-aircraft inertial navigation system
CH	Chain Home
CHL	Chain Home (low)
CIC	Combat information centre
COC	Common operations centre
COD	Carrier on-board delivery
DoD	Department of Defense (USA)
ECCM	Electronic counter-countermeasures
ECM	Electronic countermeasures
Elint	Electronic intelligence
ESD	Electronic Systems Division (US Air Force)
ESM	Electronic Support Measures
FAA	Fleet Air Arm (Royal Navy)
FASS	Forward and aft scanner system
FFT	Fast Fourier transform
FMICW	Frequency-modulated intermittent continuous-wave
HF	High frequency (2–20 MHz)
HSA	Hawker Siddeley Aviation
IFF	Identification, friend or foe
ILS	Instrument landing system
INS	Inertial navigation system
IOT&E	Initial operation test and evaluation

Jtids	Joint tactical information distribution system
kHz	Kilohertz (one thousand cycles per second)
kW	Kilowatt
LF	Low frequency (below 2 MHz)
MHz	Megahertz (one million cycles per second)
MoD	Ministry of Defence
MTI	Moving-target indicator
Nadge	Nato air-defence ground environment
Nato	North Atlantic Treaty Organization
Norad	North American air defense
ORT	Overland Radar Technology
OTH	Over-the-horizon
PDES	Pulse-Doppler elevation scan
PDNES	Pulse-Doppler non-elevation scan
PDS	Passive detection system
PRF	Pulse-repetition frequency
RAE	Royal Aircraft Establishment
RAF	Royal Air Force
RN	Royal Navy
RRE	Royal Radar Establishment
RSRE	Royal Signals and Radar Establishment
SAM	Surface-to-air missile
SAR	Synthetic aperture radar
SID	System integration development
SSR	Secondary surveillance radar
Tacan	Tactical air navigation
TDMA	Time-division multiple access
TDS	Tactical data system
TWT	Travelling-wave tube
UHF	Ultra-high frequency (200–400 MHz)
UK	United Kingdom
Ukage	United Kingdom air-defence ground environment
US	United States of America
USAF	United States Air Force
USN	United States Navy
USSR	United Soviet Socialist Republic
VHF	Very-high frequency (108–136 MHz)
VLF	Very low frequency (around 20 KHz)
VOR	VHF omni-directional range

Index